LANDMARK COLLECTOR'S LIBRARY

Stationary Steam Engines of Great Britain
The National Photographic Collection
Volume 5: The North Midlands:
Derbyshire, Leicestershire, Lincolnshire, Nottinghamshire, Staffordshire

George Watkins

The Watkins Collection in the National Monuments Record

This comprises the photographs and notes George Watkins made during a lifetime of study of the stationary steam engine.

The Steam Engine Record is an annotated set of around 1500 mounted prints of steam engines which Watkins examined in the field between 1930 and 1980. His notebooks contain a record of additional sites for which no photographs were taken, or which comprise written historical notes.
In all almost 2000 entries were made in his notebooks.
There are also albums of prints arranged by engine type. A catalogue is available.

In addition there are files of notes and other records on all aspects of historical steam technology, the cataloguing of which is in progress.

The main areas of this part of the collection are:

Records of steam engine makers.

Collection of bound trade literature.

Classified collection of data files dealing with, for example, textile mill engines, marine engines.

The collection can be inspected by appointment.
Copies of photographs and other documents are readily available.

Please contact:

NMR Enquiry & Research Services
National Monuments Record Centre
Kemble Drive
Swindon
Wilts
SN2 2GZ

STATIONARY STEAM ENGINES OF GREAT BRITAIN

THE NATIONAL PHOTOGRAPHIC COLLECTION

VOLUME 5:
THE NORTH MIDLANDS

George Watkins

Landmark Publishing

Published by

Ashbourne Hall, Cokayne Ave
Ashbourne, Derbyshire, DE6 1EJ England
Tel: (01335) 347349 Fax: (01335) 347303
e-mail: landmark@clara.net
web site: www.landmarkpublishing.co.uk

ISBN 1 901522 60 1

© George Watkins

Print: Bookcraft, Midsomer Norton, Bath

Designed by: James Allsopp

Editor: A P Woolrich

Production: C L M Porter

Front cover: SER 439B
Back cover: SER 24C
Page 3: SER 120

CONTENTS

FOREWORD
by A. P. Woolrich

George Watkins (1904-1989) spent most of his working life as a heating engineer and boilerman in Bristol. Starting in the 1930s, in his spare time he made short trips throughout Britain photographing and recording stationary steam engines. In 1965, aged 61, he was appointed a research assistant at the Centre for the Study of the History of Technology at Bath University, under Dr R. A. Buchanan, and was enabled to devote all his time adding to and classifying his collection. He was still making field trips until the late 1970s, when ill-health made travelling difficult.

He was an occasional contributor to *Model Engineer* and other periodicals, and wrote important papers for the *Transactions of the Newcomen Society*. Following his appointment to Bath University he was in much demand as a lecturer and produced a series of books based on his research. These were:

The Stationary Steam Engine (1968)

The Textile Mill Engine, 2 Vol, (1970, 1971), 2ed, (1999)

Man and the Steam Engine, (1975), 2 imp (1978) (with R. A. Buchanan)

The Industrial Archaeology of the Stationary Steam Engine, (1976) (with R. A. Buchanan)

The Steam Engine in Industry 2 vol, (1978, 1979)

On his death in February 1989 his collection was gifted to the Royal Commission on the Historical Monuments of England. It may be freely consulted at English Heritage's National Record Centre at Swindon. As well as photographs the collection comprises numerous technical notes about all manner of steam engine related topics; an incomparable archive of trade catalogues, some dating from the late nineteenth century; a collection of letters from like-minded friends, of value today for the light they shed on the history of the growth of Industrial Archaeology; lecture notes and slides. His library was left to Bath University.

He would visit a site and take illustrated notes and photographs, usually around half a dozen. His notes usually contained measured sketches of the machines and also the layouts of the premises he visited. In all, he travelled over 120,000 miles and visited nearly 2,000 sites, but in approximately 10% only took written notes. He filed sets of contact prints of each visit in binders sorted by engine type and between 1965-1971 he made a selection of the best prints for Bath University staff to print to a larger format. These were drymounted on card and annotated with details from his field notebooks and today form what is known at the Steam Engine Record. It is this collection, with notes, which forms the basis of the present series of regional books.

The Steam Engine Record is filed in numerical order, but catalogues are available listing makers, engine types and locations. When the field trips were being made the historic county names still applied, but the modern catalogues in the Search Room at Swindon allow searching by new counties and metro-politan areas, such as Cleveland and Greater Manchester. In this series, however, the historical county names have been retained.

When he began his surveys, he travelled by bicycle and train, and many were to sites he could reach readily from Bristol, but he soon graduated to a series of autocycles, on which he would pack his photographic gear and his clothing. He planned his trips meticulously during the winter months, writing to mill owners to gain permission, and then during following summer (when his boiler was shut down for maintenance), having saved up all his available leave time, would then spend two or three weeks on his travels, staying in bed-and-breakfast accommodation, or, as he became more widely known, with friends. During the autumn he would write up his notes, and begin planning the following year's trip.

He was initially interested in beam engines, but soon concentrated on the textile mill engines of mostly Lancashire and Yorkshire. In this he was greatly aided by local experts such as Frank Wightman and Arthur Roberts, who were working in these areas. Later his interest included colliery winding engines, waterworks and marine engines. During the War, when he found difficulty in both travelling far and in getting permission to enter industrial sites, he investigated water-powered sites, such as the Avon Valley brass mills, near Bristol, and the Worcestershire edge tool manufacturing sites. An area of steam technology which did not concern him was the railway locomotive, though he did record a small number of industrial locomotives and traction engines he found on his visits.

The regional distribution of the sites he visited includes most English counties and a number in Wales and Scotland. The numbers of sites he saw in the counties differ greatly, with Yorkshire, Lancashire, and the counties around Bristol predominating. This is because he had close links with other workers in those areas, and he relied on this network to learn where engines might be found. Areas where he had few contacts tended to be thinly covered.

In many counties he saw sites with a marine connection. These will be covered in Volume 10 of this series. In this context this means a steam engine which drove a vessel, whether at sea, river or canal; also preserved marine engines. Engines at waterside features such as dockside workshops are included in the regional sequence of books.

George Watkins often photographed under near impossible conditions.

Engine-room lighting was frequently indifferent, and confined space often made hard the siting of the camera for obtaining adequate perspective views. For most of the work reproduced in this series he used a tripod-mounted wooden plate camera with extension bellows which he modified to accept different lenses. In his early years he was continually experimenting with different combinations of film speeds, lenses and exposure times. Although he did eventually own a 35mm roll film camera, he was never happy with using it, and was frequently heard to grumble about the quality of modern film stock.

He used cut film, held in a dark slide, and had the films developed by a local chemist in the centres he visited so he could go back and take another if a print failed. He overcame bad lighting by having very long exposures, so was able to appear in his own prints occasionally.

The long exposures also meant he was able to 'freeze' a slow-moving engine. He did this by shielding the lens by a hand-held card or the lens cap until the engine had reached, say, top dead centre and then removing the shield momentarily. This cumulative exposure resulted in an image of a still engine, and such was his deftness of touch and impeccable timing, that it is very hard to see any kind of shake or blemish on the photographs. He was adept at 'painting with light' - utilising hand-held electric lead-lights with which he could illuminate different parts of the engine successively.

He made copies from his negatives at home for distribution to his friends by using a simple contact-print frame and developer chemicals. There are many small sets of his prints in private hands.

The lenses he used were not bloomed to prevent 'flaring' of the image caused by extraneous light from windows or hanging light bulbs, and some of the photographs reproduced are marred by this. He made his selection of prints for the Steam Engine Record on the basis of their historical and technical importance, and not on their artistic quality.

His photographs are a unique record

of the end of stationary steam power in this country, being made at a time when electrification, nationalisation and trade depression created wholesale changes in the physical structure of the industrial landscape. They are an invaluable resource to our understanding of the reality of industrial activity, and will interest, as well as the technical historian, the local historian and model-maker. It is good to know they are being published, for this in turn will focus attention on the rest of his reference collection, which deserves to be more widely known and used.

ISSES (The International Stationary Steam Engine Society) is publishing a number of volumes devoted to George Watkins and his work. The first volume was published mid-2002. It includes a biography of George Watkins, reminiscences by his friends, and copies of a number of his earlier writings, including some unpublished ones from the 1930's, and an account of the Watkins collection at Swindon,

Details and prices may be obtained from:

Mr John Cooper, 73 Coniston Way, Blossom Hill,
Bewdley, Worcestershire,
DY12 2QA
Tel: 01299 402946
Email:
John.Cooper@isses2.freeserve.co.uk
Web site: www.steamenginesociety.org

The sites are in alphabetical order of geographical location, and then site name and no attempt has been made to place them by precise grid references. As work on this series has progressed it has become plain that the locations are sometimes wrong, particularly county names. This is because George used the nearest post town, which was sometimes in the next county. This has caused problems when allocating the entries to the books of this regional series, so work has been done closely cross checking the remaining original SER cards and revising the headings as necessary.

Each entry heading has an illustration number for this volume, the location, revised as necessary and the Steam Engine Record (SER) number. This latter number is the key for accessing the copies of the field notebooks and the files of additional photographs in the National Monuments Record at Swindon.

The remaining page comprises brief illustrated notes to explain detail and a glossary of some of the terms he uses.

DERBYSHIRE

In Derbyshire he saw a varied selection of sites, covering coal mining, water and sewage pumping, pottery manufacture, agricultural contracting, iron manufacture, chemicals processing and brick making.

LEICESTERSHIRE

Here he saw coal mining, water supply, flour milling, textile manufacture and brick making.

LINCOLNSHIRE

A major feature of this county was sites concerned with land drainage, particularly by the scoop wheel. Other sites in the mostly agricultural country included, sawmills, oilseed processing, maltings, and brewing and in addition some concerning steel making.

NOTTINGHAMSHIRE

Coalmining formed a large part of the sites he visited in Nottinghamshire, as might be expected, but he also saw several important water supply sites, as well as land drainage and pottery manufacture.

STAFFORDSHIRE

In Staffordshire he saw a number of pottery, brick and tile manufactories, as well as coal mining. He also saw agricultural contractors, some iron and steel manufactories, and several water supply and ewage pumping stations.

Beam engine, the original form as made by Boulton and Watt. This form owed its existence to the fact that all the earlier steam engines were used for pumping water, the beam forming a convenient means of attachment for the pump rods.

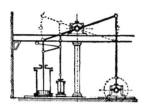

Horizontal Engine, with open frame cast iron bedplate, a type much used for all sizes of engine for general purposes. The bed-plate frame was of a U section, and was bolted down to a foundation of masonry or brickwork, the cylinder, main bearing and guides being bolted to the bed-plate.

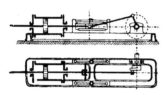

Vertical engine, a type used extensively for both large and small engines; it had the advantage of occupying little floor space. An endless number of varieties of this type was developed, and was the generally accepted type for marine screw-propeller engines.

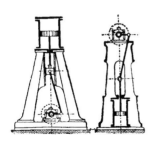

Corliss frame or Girder Engine, a type of horizontal engine. This example had a bored guide, but they were also made with flat-planed guides. In both cases the guides were formed in the main casting or girder which connects the cylinder to the main bearing. There were many varieties of this type.

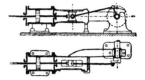

Self contained horizontal engines, with bent or slotted out cranks. This type, largely used for small power short-stroke engines had the cylinder bolted on to the end of an open bedplate, which was widened out at the other end to take both bearings of the crank shaft, so that the flywheel might be keyed on either side. The guides were usually formed in the bedplate, the boring out of the guides and facing of the end flange being done at the same setting.

Oscillating Engines, formerly much used as marine engines. Originally developed for driving paddle wheels, this type has also been used for driving screw propellers. Uncommon in land use.

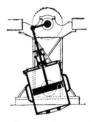

Steeple engine, formerly used for driving paddle wheels. A variety of this type had been used for small powers, and was known as the Table Engine.

Beam Engine, Woolf's Compound. Two unequal cylinders side by side, at one end of the beam. Many pumping engines were of this type.

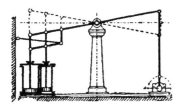

McNaught Compound Beam Engine. This system consisted of a small cylinder (high-pressure cylinder), placed at the opposite end of the beam to the larger cylinder, was introduced by McNaught for increasing the power of existing engines. The high-pressure cylinder was the one added, the original cylinder being the low-pressure cylinder. The power of the engine was thus increased by increase of boiler pressure and the addition of the new small cylinder, to which the boiler was admitted. (See glossary for more details).

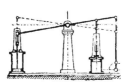

Inclined Frame Engines, used extensively for paddle steamers in several different varieties, usually compound engines.

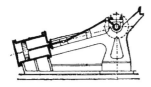

A Double-Cylinder Engine, derived from the above, with the cylinder inclined at an angle of about 45°, was occasionally used for driving rolling mills in bar iron works.

Radial Engines. (Brotherhood type) A recent type, of which there were many varieties, in both 3 and 4 cylinder configurations. These were used for driving fans, steam launches and other applications requiring speed and compactness.

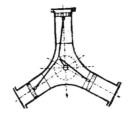

Central Valve Engines (Willans type) A modern design, single acting, compound or triple expansion configuration; a special feature was the hollow piston rod and central valve. Extensively used for driving dynamos coupled direct on to the armature shaft.

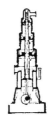

Various ways of arranging cylinders and cranks in double and three-cylinder compound and triple expansion engines

Double cylinder, with cranks at 180°

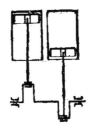

Three-cylinder engine, with cranks at 120°

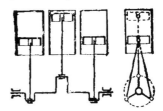

Compound Woolf engine with cranks together

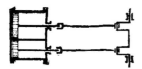

Compound Woolf engine with cranks at 180⁰

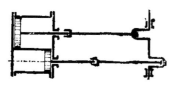

Compound Tandem engine with receiver

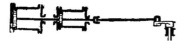

Compound engine with cylinders side by side with receiver cranks at 90⁰

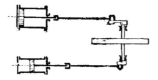

Triple expansion engine with cylinders side by side; cranks at 120⁰

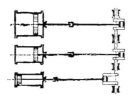

Triple expansion engine, semi-tandem; two cranks at 90⁰

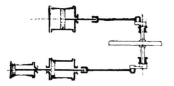

Simple slide valve
This consisted of an inverted metal box sliding on the ported face of the cylinder. It controlled the admission and exhaust of the steam to both ends of the cylinder and exhausted beneath the box valve

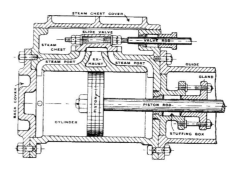

Simple piston valve
This consisted of a turned bobbin, working in a bored liner. It worked on the same principle as the slide valve.

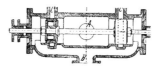

Simple valve gears
These valves were operated by simple eccentric motions of various patterns, and many allowed variable cut-off of the steam as well as reversing.

The Corliss
This was a semi-circular semi-rotating valve working in a bored liner. Separate valves were provided for steam and exhaust at each end of the cylinder, so there were four in number. A trip gear operated the valves.

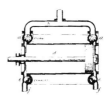

Drop valves

These were circular with taper faces, which fitted upon similar faces fitted to the cylinder. The faces were ground together to make them steam tight. The valves were lifted to admit steam and dropped by the trip gear to cut off the admission. A variety of this pattern was simple bobbins fitted with piston rings.

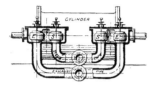

The Uniflow

This had admission valves only since the steam exhausted through a ring of ports in the centre of the cylinder barrel.

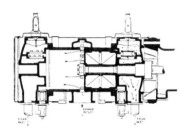

BOILERS

Cornish boilers contained a single flue

 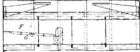

Lancashire boilers contained twin flues

 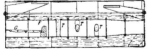

Multitibular boilers were of various types including the locomotive

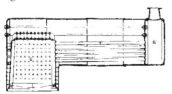

Vertical boilers were of various types. Used in very small plants

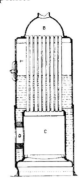

Watertube boilers were of various types.

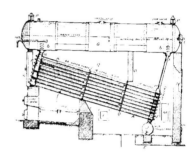

POWER TRANSMISSION

Rope drives, taking power from the engine to the floors of a mill, were usual in textile mills. In older mills power was often transmitted by a vertical shaft.

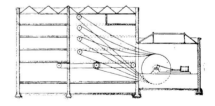

Flat belts of leather or rubberized canvas drove individual machines from a line shaft powered by the rope drive.

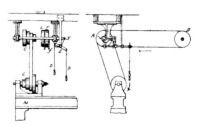

MINING

Winding engines were almost invariably made with two cylinders having cranks at **90⁰**, allowing good control by the engine driver. A winding engine was required to work intermittently, starting a heavy load from rest, bringing this load up with great velocity, and bringing it to rest again. This had to be done at great speed in a short time, since a great number of winds were needed daily to raise an economic quantity of coal. For this, the engine needed to be powerful and to be under precise control of the engineman at all times.

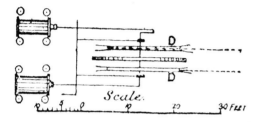

Balancing was done by fixing a rope similar to the winding rope to the bottom of each cage, the rope hanging in a loop down the pit shaft, ensuring a perpetual balance-weight equal to the winding-rope.

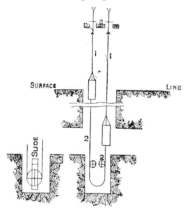

Another method of balancing was by means of the scroll or spiral drum. As the engine proceeded to wind up, the rope was wound in spiral grooves on a continually increasing diameter of drum. The other rope to the descending cage was wound off at an opposing rate so creating a counterbalance. The variation in diameter of the two sides of the drum had the effect of loading the engine proportional to the effort it needed at different stages of the wind.

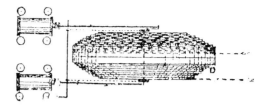

Winding was done by steam, utilising different types of pithead gear.

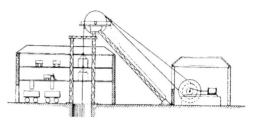

Ventilation was done by various patterns of steam driven rotary fan.

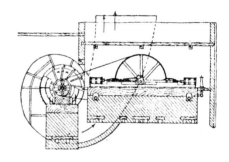

GLOSSARY

Air pump. This removed the condensed water and air contained in the steam. It was normally driven by the engine itself.

Arbor. An axle or spindle.

Barring. This was the action of gently rotating the engine to make possible adjustments during maintenance. It was done by a lever mechanism which engaged in a series of holes cast in the face or side of the flywheel rim. A variation involved a hand or small steam engine-driven gear engaging in gear teeth cast on the inside of the flywheel rim.

Calender. A finishing machine designed to impart lustre and smoothness to woven fabrics. It comprised a series of rolls geared vertically, through which the cloth ran.

Condensers. These were airtight chambers into which the exhaust steam passed for cooling back to warm water. Cooling was by a jet of cold water which mixed with the condensate, or, in the surface type, the cold water passed through a number of small tubes to condense the steam outside them.

Count. The measure of yarns by length and weight stating how many hanks of a given length will weigh a pound: the higher the number, the finer the yarn. There were different units of length for different yarns, e.g. cotton, wool, and jute and, in the wool trade, different locations.

Dram or tram. A wheeled tub for conveying coal at the colliery.

Duff coal. Small coal unsuitable for retail sale. Used for firing boilers at collieries.

Economiser. A system of pre-heating boiler feed-water, using the heat of the waste gases in the boiler flues. First invented in 1843 by Edward Green of Wakefield, Yorks.

Edge tools. These were any kind of hand tool with a sharp cutting edge, such as a spade, hoe, sickle or scythe. A strip of toughened steel was forged as a sandwich between softer metal, and then sharpened. This was an ancient craft, some of the sites utilising water-powered tilt hammers.

Egg-ended boiler. A horizontal cylindrical boiler with hemispherical ends and no flues. At early pattern, superseded by the Cornish and Lancashire types.

Flitches. The two halves of the beam of a beam engine. Originally cast solid, beams were sometimes made in two halves and kept apart by spacers and bolts.

Glands. These were recessed bosses in the cylinder cover or valve chest of a steam engine or pump which were fitted with fibre or metal packing. They allowed the rods to work freely without leaking steam or water.

Governor. This device controlled the speed of the engine, if it was too fast or too slow, by regulating the steam supply. There were many patterns but all depended on rotating weights which adjusted the control mechanism.

Grid. The National Grid, the national electricity supply system, was begun in the 1920s. Before it became very widespread by the 1950s, many small towns and larger businesses generated their own supplies, with varying supply standards.

Hoppit or hoppet. A large basket used in mining.

Lodge. A pond located near a mill's engine-house which held the engine's condensing water. More common where the site was not previously water powered.

Manhattan engine. This was a design which coupled a horizontal and a vertical engine driving to the same crank pin. The idea surfaced around 1870 and reached its zenith in the engines driving the Manhattan (New York) power stations in the early 1900s. A number were made by various makers for use in Britain, driving textile mills, rolling mills and London Tramways power generation.

McNaughting was patented by William McNaught of Glasgow in 1845. Piston loads were thus opposed, so reducing stresses on the beam centre. The fitting of high pressure boilers and compound working gave great economy.

Mule. Cotton spinning machine, invented by Crompton, so named because it incorporated the roller-drawing principle of Arkwright's water frame and the carriage drawing of Hargreave's spinning jenny. The first successful self-acting mule was invented by Richard Roberts 1830.

Non-dead centre engines. These were vertical or horizontal engines in which two parallel cylinders were coupled to a single crank pin by a triangular connecting rod, and had the advantage of starting at almost any crank position. Twin or quadruple cylinder compound engines were common. Their heyday was 1880-1907.

Northrop loom. An automatic loom invented by 1894 by J. H. Northrop in the USA.

Overwinding gear. This was an apparatus to stop a winding engine lifting a cage beyond the pit bank and damaging itself and contents on the pit frame. Various systems were used.

Process steam. This was steam after it had left the engine and before it was condensed. It was used in the plant for other purposes such as central heating, heating dye vats, drying paper.

Rastrick Boiler. A pattern of vertical boiler which utilised the waste heat from wrought iron-making processes.

Ring spinning. A system where the spinning spindle revolves within a ring, with a small steel hoop on the flange of the ring to govern the winding-on of the thread.

Room and Power. The term means that a capitalist established a factory with a power supply (usually steam), and heating, and rented out space to small craftsmen or manufacturers. Each floor had a drive shaft taken from the engine from which individual machines, owned and worked by the tenants, were driven.

Shear. Mechanical scissors used for cropping billets of steel during the rolling process.

Sizing. The stiffening of fabrics with various pastes or starches.

Slow banking. This involved the means of controlling the winding engine carefully to allow precise location of the cage at the finish of the wind.

Tentering or stentering. This was the action of stretching cloth whilst drying to ensure all the threads were in line. Originally done by hand, latterly by machine.

SOURCES

Definitions and illustrations used have been drawn from:

Wilfred Lineham, *A text book of Mechanical Engineering*, 9ed, 1906.

Arnold Lupton, *Mining*, 3ed, 1906.

William S. Murphy, The *Textile Industries*, 8 vol, 1910.

Herman Haeder and H. H. P. Powles, *Handbook on the Steam Engine*, 4ed, 1914.

More detailed technical information about engine design may be found in:

Colin Bowden, 'The stationary steam engine: a critical bibliography', *Industrial Archaeology Review*, XV, (1992-3), pp 177-194.

George Watkins, *The Stationary Steam Engine*, 1968.

George Watkins, *The Textile Mill Engine*, 2 vol, 1970, 1971 (reprinted Landmark Publishing, 1 vol, 1999).

George Watkins, & R. A. Buchanan, *Man and the Steam Engine*, 1975, 2ed 1978.

R. A. Buchanan & George Watkins, *The Industrial Archaeology of the Stationary Steam Engine*, (1976) This is a very authoritative account of the evolution of design and construction.

George Watkins. *The Steam Engine in Industry*, 2 vol, (1978, 1978). The linking passages describing the application of steam to different industries are specially valuable.

Transactions of the Newcomen Society, especially:

Arnold Throp 'Some notes on the history of the Uniflow Steam Engine', vol 43 (1970-71) pp 19-39.

George Watkins, 'The development of the Steam Winding Engine' vol 50, (1978-79), pp 11-24.

James L. Wood, 'The introduction of the Corliss Engine into Britain', vol 52, (1980-81) pp 1-13.

R. L. Hills, 'The Uniflow engine, a reappraisal' vol 57, (1985-6) , pp 59-77.

R. W. M. Clouston, 'The development of the Babcock Boiler in Britain up to 1939', vol 58, (1986-87), pp 75-87.

James L. Wood. 'The Sulzer steam engine comes to Britain', vol 59, (1987-88), pp 129-152.

Stationary Power (The Journal of the International Steam Engine Society), especially:

William D. Sawyer, Corliss Man and engine, 2 vol, 1994, (JISSES 10), 1997, (JISSES 13).

DERBYSHIRE

1. Bamford, Robert Marsland & Co, Bamford Mill   SER 994a

Type:	Horizontal single tandem condensing
Photo Taken:	1959
Maker & Date:	J. Musgrave & Sons, Bolton, 1907
Cylinder/dimensions:	16in and 30in x 2ft 6in – Stegen drop piston valves
Hp: 500	*Rpm:* 103 *Psi:* 160
Service:	Cotton doubling mill drive by ropes

This was an old established site, once corn milling and then to cotton doubling, originally with good water power and later assisted by a beam engine. The whole was re-organised and later the mill extended in 1907 and the drives were completely altered. The original gear drives took power from the new engine, which drove in several directions to the old and the new shafting. It was always well kept, Marsland being a highly responsible concern. It was said on the site that the new engine had driven on to the old beam engine gearing for some years. Using superheated steam, it was highly economical, running the whole plant latterly when there was little water for the water turbines after the water was taken for Sheffield town supply. It was retained by the new owners after it ceased work as a doubling mill in the 1960s.

2. Bamford, Robert Marsland & Co, Bamford Mill   SER 994b

Type:	Two water turbines
Photo Taken:	1959
Maker & Date:	Gilbert Gilkes & Co, Kendal, 1920s?
Cylinder/dimensions:	No sizes available
Hp: 20 hp & 42 hp	*Rpm:* *Psi:*
Service:	Mill drive by ropes. Assisted steam engine – driving into same shafting

There was considerable water power on the site for over a century, using water wheels, and in the late 19th century, the water wheel was replaced by turbines, one of which developed 140 h.p. Latterly however, the water rights were acquired by the local corporation for town supply, only leaving the minimal compensation supply available for the turbines seen in the print This was regularly used as far as possible, driving into the mill shafting until the mill was closed.

3. Chesterfield, Sheepbridge Coal & Iron Co   SER 393

Type:	Single cylinder vertical non-condensing
Maker & Date:	Unknown, c1860s?
Photo Date:	1951
Cylinder/dimensions:	8in x 1ft 4in – Slide valve.
Hp: 8-9	*Rpm:* 60-70 *Psi:* ?
Service:	Pit pony feed preparation plant

This was an old corn mill latterly used for the preparation of feed for the ponies used in Glapwell, Langwith and other Sheepbridge Co. collieries. The plant comprised chaff cutters, a hoist and possibly bean crushers etc., and was in use as long as ponies were used i.e. until the 1940s. It was a neat but plain design and very well kept, requiring little maintenance, and used two or three times a week. The crankshaft was 7ft above the floor with belt drives throughout.

3

4. Chesterfield, Sheepbridge Rolling Mills   SER 1400

Type:	Double cylinder horizontal non-condensing
Maker & Date:	Sheepbridge Co., Workshops, 1910
Photo Taken:	1970
Cylinder/ dimensions:	32in x 3ft 6in – Piston valves
Hp: 700	*Rpm:* 70 *Psi:* 80
Service:	Metal section rolling. Coupled direct to roll shaft

This was the last of the three engines on the site, the others having gone, together with the iron and steel making and rolling plant, and this one was disused and the mills were to be sold in 1971. The engine was unlikely to be sold as it was not powerful enough for the purchasers of the rolling mills. The engines were very well made and strong, and there was little evidence that any heavy repairs had ever been necessary. The counterbalanced cranks helped the general running, as the speed was often high in small sections. The works had blast furnaces, and extensive puddling plant in the 1930s, but the site was disused in 1972.

5. Chinley, J. J. Hadfield & Co   SER 1228

Type:	Horizontal cross compound
Maker & Date:	G. Saxon Ltd, Manchester, 1926, No 515
Photo Taken:	1966
Cylinders/dimensions:	Abt 16in and 31in x 3ft 6in – Corliss valves
Hp: 450	*Rpm:* 90 *Psi:* 120
Service:	Was mill drive by 12 ropes, now alternator

This was almost certainly the last full-sized mill engine made by Saxons, and originally drove the mill shaft by a rope drive back over the engine. It was superseded by a pass-out turbine in 1937, with all-electric drives later, and later was coupled to an alternator by chain drive, and was only used if the turbine and the later Grid current supply failed. It was unusual for Saxons in that the condenser and air pump were on floor level, whereas Saxons usually placed them below the engine. Also the air pump was of a ram type, whereas Saxons usually used a bucket form of air pump. It was very little used in the 1960s, and was probably scrapped by 1970.

6. Church Gresley, Cadley Hill Colliery   SER 1221a

Type:	Double cylinder vertical
Maker & Date:	Maker and date unknown
Photo Taken:	1965
Cylinder/dimensions:	21ft x 5ft 0in – Piston valves
Hp:?	*Rpm:* 32 *Psi:* 80
Service:	Coal winding. 3 shafts. Depths: 825ft, 444ft & 552ft

This was one of the Hall's group of collieries, and for many years, the engine wound from the three shafts noted above, by three drums of different diameters upon the one crankshaft. All three were up-cast shafts and were winding coal. It was as simple as possible, without expansion gear or cut off valves, and with plain piston valves driven by Stephenson's link motion. In 1921, the arrangements were altered by putting in a horizontal double cylinder engine to wind the two shafts of No. 1 mine (825ft deep), leaving the vertical engine to deal with No. 2 (444ft) and No. 3 (552ft) deep. There was also a Bever Dorling fan and engine of unknown design, and a twin horizontal engine on the surface driving haulage ropes which went down the shaft. There were 6 or 8 boilers at one time.

7. *Church Gresley, Cadley Hill Colliery, No 1 Shaft*   SER 1221b

Type:	Double cylinder horizontal
Maker & Date:	Maker and date unknown
Photo Taken:	1965
Cylinders:	24in x 4ft 0in – Slide valves
Hp:	*Rpm*: 32 *Psi: 80*
Service:	Coal winding

A plain colliery winder with no special features, this did however have open type eccentric rods and resembled Thornewill and Warham's design, with the arched frame at the front of the guides, and the straight angular topped guide bars. Nothing however was known of its origin for certain. This, too, was to go as steam was phased out.

8. *Church Gresley, Gresleywood Colliery, No1 Shaft*   SER 1363a

Type:	Double cylinder horizontal
Maker & Date:	Thornewill & Warham, 1897
Photo Taken:	1968
Cylinders:	36in x 6ft 0in
Hp:	*Rpm*: 30 *Psi*: 120
Service:	Coal winding, shaft 334yds deep, 5 tons coal per wind, 18ft rope drum

This was very little altered in a long run of heavy use, outside of a new rope drum and metallic rod packings. There were 18 revolutions per wind, with two cages on each of the two decks, with up to 90 winds per hour at full speed working. The No 2 winder was a Worsley Mesnes with internal piston cut-off valves and was new in 1923. There were two mixed pressure steam turbines (an alternator and air compressor). The whole was well kept. An interesting feature of some engines in this area was that the cage depth indicator figures read from 0 to 16, the meeting point of the cages in the shaft, and then back to 0 for the landing point. In most areas the indicator ran on, without figures at all usually, but any figures of depth were otherwise continuous. Governor controlled cut-off gear was fitted, but latterly disused.

9. *Church Gresley, Gresleywood Colliery, No 2 Shaft*   SER 1363b

Type:	Horizontal double cylinder
Maker & Date:	Worsley Mesnes Co., Wigan, 1923
Photo Taken:	1968
Cylinders:	24in x 4ft 0in – Piston Valves
Hp:	*Rpm*: 45 *Psi*: 120
Service:	Coal winding. Rope drum 10ft diameter

The new engine at No 2 shaft was fitted with a small drum and ran quite fast, and was fitted with internal piston cut-off valves which gave good economy. The only alterations were added safety gear, and a casing round the rope drum. It was again very well kept, and painted green like No 1. It was probably the last new engine to be installed in the area, although there were possibly several new cylinders put on later.

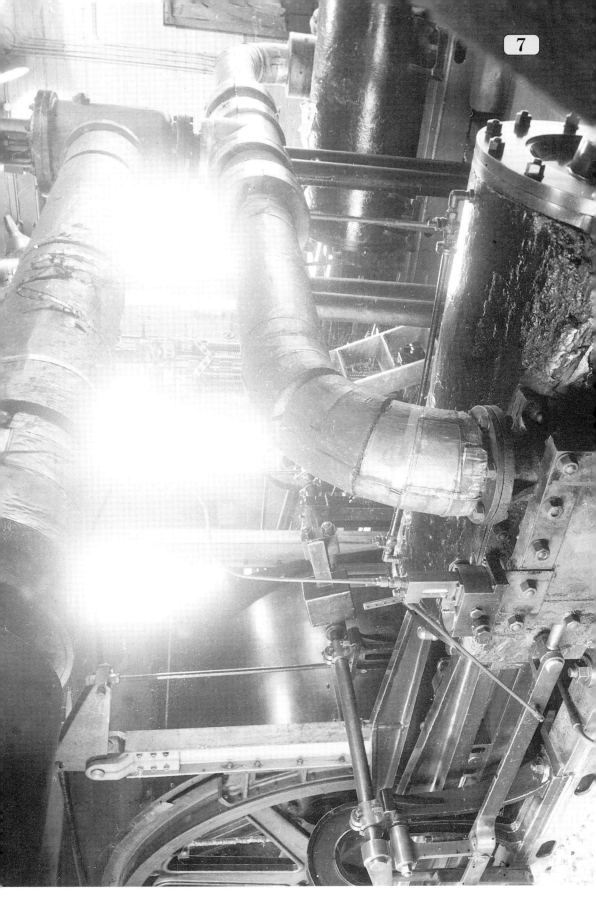

10. Clay Cross, Clay Cross Colliery   SER 188a

Type:	Cornish type beam
Maker & Date:	Butterley Co, 1862
Photo Taken:	1937
Cylinders:	84in x 10ft 0in. Beam: 36ft 6in x 3ft 4in deep
Hp:	*Rpm:* *Psi:*
Service:	Pit pump.
	Shaft 418ft deep; 18in bucket lift to 270ft 18in ram to 210ft.
	18in ram to top.

This was Howes's celebrated engine, designed after the Hartley colliery disaster of 1862 to have wrought iron slab beams which have the largest that had been made to date. Each weighed 7½ tons and was 2 in thick, each flitch being a single slab. The pit water was too bad to be used for the boilers, but there was a feeder of good water at the 210 ft level, and this was pumped by a separate pump off the main rods, for use in the boilers, and the local houses. Electric pumping had been installed in the 1920s, and the beam engines long disused, although available as standby to avoid drowning.

11. Clay Cross, Clay Cross Colliery   SER 188b

Type:	Horizontal twin cylinder non-condensing
Maker & Date:	The Clay Cross Co, 1870s?
Photo Taken:	1937
Cylinders:	16in x 2ft 0in – Slide valves
Hp:	*Rpm:* *Psi:*
Service:	Surface or drift haulage

This was typical of the plain designs adopted when a large concern made engines for its own use. The rectangular forged connecting rods, and the slide valves which appeared to be of the hollow design, with the steam entry from the back, and the method of driving the link motion from a pin in the connecting rod to a drag link and small lay shaft were all interesting individual features. It was later scrapped together with much historically interesting plant when the coal and iron trade was reorganised.

12. Cressbrook, Dickie & Co, Cotton Doublers   SER 1194

Type:	Mill buildings
Maker & Date:	No other data
Photo Taken:	1965
Cylinders:	
Hp:	*Rpm:* *Psi:*
Service:	Early cotton mill

Cressbrook was one of the early cotton mill sites of the period, when to secure water, the mills were placed wherever it was available. This site was always partly driven by water, with auxiliary steam drive as the water fell off in the latter part of the 19th century. The spinning and weaving sections are the nearer buildings, and in the background is the Apprentices' House. There, the small children were housed and trained to work in the cotton mills, since there was no local population in the remote places where there was water power. The labour force was created by absorbing Poor House children and orphans to be trained and housed at the mills. For all the sorry abuses that were known to arise, it was better than the wasted lives of the desperate poor of the times, whose lot was often starvation in ghetto housing in the rapidly growing cities.

13. Crich, Ilkeston & Heanor Waterworks, Whatstandwell Pumping Station — SER 809

Type:	Three inverted vertical triple expansion
Maker & Date:	Tangyes Ltd., Birmingham, 1903
Photo Taken:	1956
Cylinders:	16in, 24in and 36in x 3ft 0in – Slide valves
Hp:	*Rpm:* *Psi:*
Service:	Town supply to reservoirs

These were very plain engines driving ram pumps below the engine room, and were virtually three separate engines joined by flanged couplings on the crankshaft, and flanges on the sections of the bed. Belliss and Morcom high speed engines and gear driven turbine pumps were installed later, and extensive water softening plant was added. By 1955 all of the steam plant had been scrapped, and at least one of the Belliss driven pumps was then coupled to a motor, and other electric pumps added.

14. Cromford, Leawood Pumping Station, Cromford Canal — SER 56

Type:	Cornish beam
Maker & Date:	Graham & Co, Milton Iron Works, 1849
Photo Taken:	1936
Cylinders:	36in x 8ft 6in. Beam 27ft 0in long
Hp:	*Rpm:* *Psi:*
Service:	Pump for water supply to canal and locomotive water troughs. Plunger pump 56in x 8ft 6in, 30ft head. 850 gals per stroke.

This was works No. 57, believed to have been there since 1849. It was little used in later years. The whole engine was inside of the house, i.e. the pumps were inside as well. It was said to have cost £1,200 in 1849, and few repairs were ever needed, other than new boilers. There were two of locomotive type installed in the 1920s.

15. Derby, Walter Evans & Co, Darley Abbey — SER 1279

Type:	Horizontal single tandem condensing
Maker & Date:	John Musgrave & Sons, Bolton, 1897
Photo Taken:	1966
Cylinders:	14in and 28in x 3ft 0in – Corliss valves
Hp: 250	*Rpm:* 80 *Psi:* 120
Service:	Mill drive

This was an extensive water power site, with several buildings each with water wheels, and interconnection of the shafting between them. Latterly there were five water turbines, of 60 to 100 h.p. each, most of them driving into the main-shaft of the long mill building. There may have been a beam engine, but the Musgrave engine in the end of the long mill was connected to the main-shaft. The mechanical drives were very complex, but certainly the water power was used until road alterations stopped all water supply in 1969. The position of the business was adversely affected by this, with the future unknown. The engine was a standard Musgrave design. In 1917, a suction gas plant with 180 hp twin cylinder horizontal engine was installed in another mill building, which had its own water turbine and there was an underground shaft 150 ft. long coupling this and the long mill building.

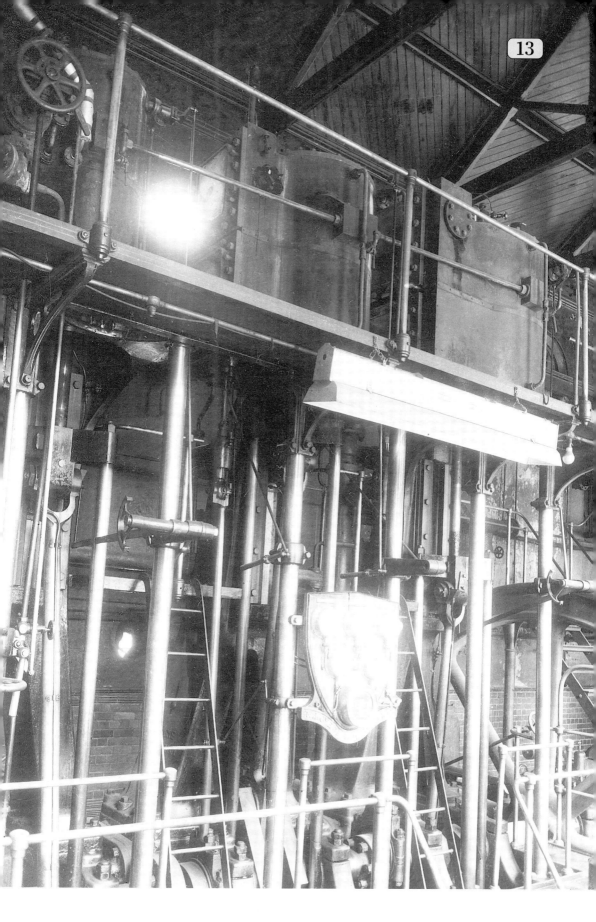

16. Grassmoor, Chesterfield, Grassmoor Colliery   SER 1170

Type:	Double cylinder horizontal
Maker & Date:	Oliver & Co, Chesterfield, 1880s
Photo Taken:	1964
Cylinders:	30in x 6ft 0in - Cornish valves. New 1920
Hp:	*Rpm:* 30 *Psi:* 80
Service:	Coal winding. Shaft 390 yards deep. Drum 20ft diameter

Grassmoor was a very large pit when owned by the Barnes family, with 5 shafts of varying depth, all drawing coal from several seams; a Cornish beam pump, air compressors, and electric generating plants, as well as coke ovens. There were then 26 Lancashire and two Babcock water tube boilers. The Black Shale pit was the busiest, winding up to 75 journeys per hour from 440 yards deep. The pit was a shadow of this by 1966, with one winding engine, a few boilers and pit head baths.

17. Hartington, D S F Refractories, Friden   SER 1480

Type:	Horizontal twin cylinder non-condensing
Maker & Date:	Robey and Co, Lincoln No 22110, c. 1890s
Photo Taken:	1975
Cylinders:	$16\frac{1}{2}$in x 2ft 6in – Slide valves
Hp: 150	*Rpm:* 90 *Psi:* 80
Service:	General plant drive

Bought secondhand from a colliery (where it had probably driven the ventilating fan) in 1925, this engine ran at Friden day and night for 45 years, averaging some 130 hours per week, finally working 8-10 hours daily. The load was very heavy when the grinding pan was loaded every 30 minutes with hard heavy lumps of clay which were ground to a rough powder. This slipped the 12in driving belt at the start. It also drove the hoist for the large lumps and two other crushers as needed. The large pan mill contained 2 stone rollers each weighing 5 tons. This engine must have run day and night for over 75 years yet was still quiet and efficient (1976).

18. Little Eaton, Derby Waterworks   SER 25a

Type:	Two Cornish beam
Maker & Date:	R & W Hawthorn, Newcastle upon Tyne, 1849
Photo Taken:	1935
Cylinders:	48in x 8ft 0in
Hp:?	*Spm:* 8-10 *Psi:* 15
Service:	Town supply to high and low level districts. Pumped 2,400,000 gallons per day to 170ft head. 18in ram pumps

These were the original units which pumped to the earlier lower town areas. They had 4 Cornish boilers and were in regular use as standby until the electrical pumps were installed in the 1930s. The Gothic framing was very attractive, When broken up the steam side was in good order, but the pumps were not.

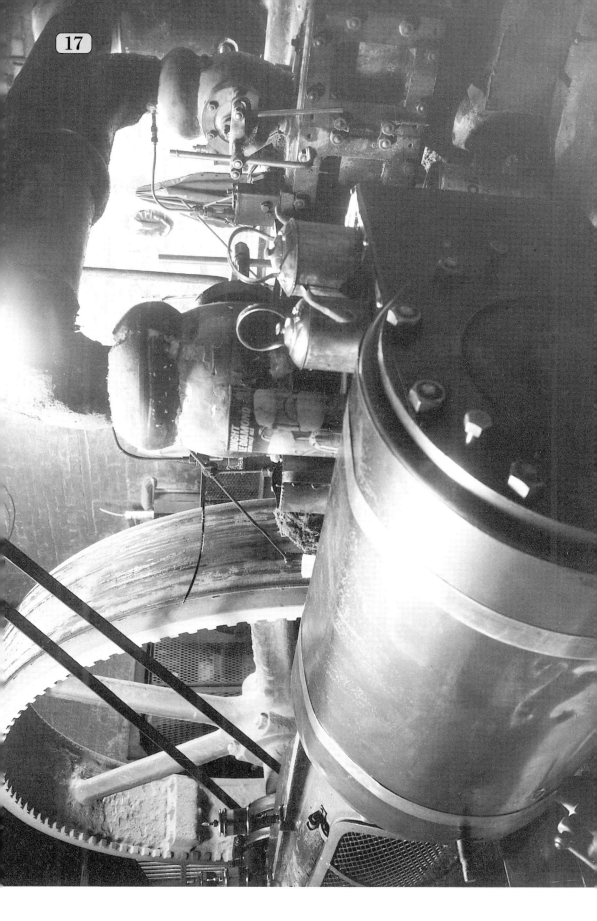

19. Little Eaton, Derby Waterworks   SER 25b

Type:	Two rotative beam
Maker & Date:	Kitson and Co, Leeds, 1873 & 1877
Photo Taken:	1935
Cylinders:	36in x 7ft 0in – Drop valves. Beams 25ft long. Flywheel 25ft diameter.
Hp: 100	*Rpm*:$16^1/_2$ *Psi*: ?
Service:	Town supply to the higher levels. Pumped 3,000,000 gallons per day
	1 bucket and plunger pump 17in ram and 24in bucket x 3ft 6in stroke

These pumped to the high level only and like the Cornish units were finished in a Gothic motif for the cast iron framing, and the forged ends of the parallel motion, connecting and pump rods.

20. Morton, nr Clay Cross, Morton Colliery   SER 1197a

Type:	Double cylinder horizontal
Maker & Date:	A. Handyside, Derby, No 88-9, 1865
Photo Taken:	1965
Cylinders:	30in x 5ft 0in – Slide valves
Hp:?	*Rpm*: 28 *Psi*: 65
Service:	Coal winding. No 5 shaft 350 yards deep. Coal 250 yards Rope drum 15ft diameter

This was the oldest winding engine in regular use in 1965 when the colliery was closed, and the engine is now preserved at the Leicester Museum although not on exhibition yet. The engine was in continuous usage and except for alterations to the drum, and additional safety gear, remained as built. Morton was a busy colliery in the Clay Cross ground, and in full production turned 5-6,000 tons of coal per week from No. 5 and 6 shafts, each with similar engines. The maximum was 1,300 tons in one shift of $7^1/_2$ hours. The engines were interesting in that the Stephenson's link motion was operated from a short lay-shaft on the engine bed, which was driven from a pin in the middle of the connecting rod, a very early design; also the flat slide valves were arranged to admit the steam through the back of the valve, and not into the valve chest.

21. Morton, nr Clay Cross, Morton Colliery   SER 1197b

Type:	Ventilating fan.
Maker & Date:	The Waddle Patent Fan & Engineering Co, Llanelly, 1890
Photo Taken:	1965
Cylinders:	Fan 40ft diameter
Hp:	*Rpm*: *Psi*:
Service:	Mine ventilation. Capacity 75,000 cfm at $1^1/_2$ water gauge

The colliery was ventilated from its sinking in 1865 to 1890 by a furnace, and the Waddle was then installed, possibly as the workings were extending, and connections were made with other of the numerous Clay Cross collieries. The Waddle was the largest diameter fan used in colliery work, and the firm made up to 50 ft. for the largest outputs. The rotational speed was low, about 45 rpm, and less in the largest ones, but some trouble did develop from the centrifugal stresses at the rim, as the patches seen on the photograph suggest. The vanes were finely curved, and the line of rivets for one can be seen in the second blade visible. The fan was directly connected to the engine crank shaft. The engine room was under the roof at the left-hand side.

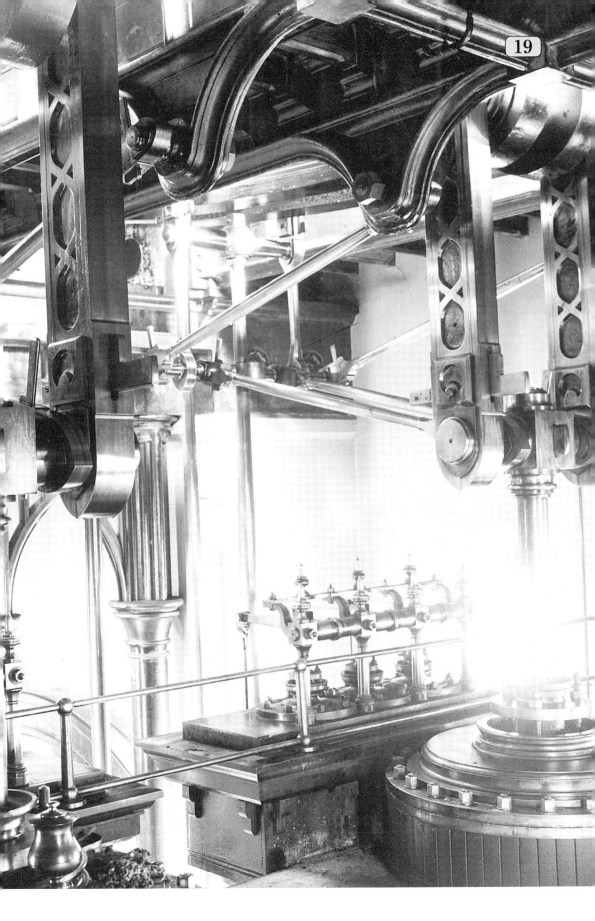

22. Morton, nr Clay Cross, Morton Colliery   SER 1197c

Type:	Horizontal single cylinder non-condensing
Maker & Date:	The Waddle Paten`t Fan & Engineering Co, Llanelly, 1890
Photo Taken:	1965
Cylinders:	30in x 4ft 0in – Slide valve
Hp: 180	*Rpm:* 45 *Psi:* 65
Service:	Fan drive engine

This was a typical colliery fan engine of the old school, plain, solid and totally reliable. It probably never had a breakdown in the 60 years it served as the main fan, until a later type Waddle, with a 200 h.p. motor was installed in 1950. The engine was fitted with a Meyer-type cut-off valve on the main slide valve. It had not been without repairs however, as there is a patch visible on the bed, and stiffeners have been added to the crankshaft bearing pedestal, but such were frequent incidents where subsidence occurred. It could not be moved, and was scrapped with the other plant.

23. Morton, nr Clay Cross, Morton Colliery   SER 1197d

Type:	General view
Maker & Date:	No other data
Photo Taken:	1965
Cylinders:	
Hp:	*Rpm:* *Psi:*
Service:	Colliery, Clay Cross Co., No 5 & 6

Except that the original wooden headgear has been replaced by a concrete structure the scene has little altered since the Waddle fan replaced the original furnace ventilation in 1890. The fan engine was in the low house at the right hand side of the rotor. The pit head was covered-in around the headgear, with the boilers away, near to the winding engine and the chimney, the latter probably being rebuilt in later years. The whole was typical of a company-owned pit, simple and practical. The site was cleared when coal mining ceased in the 1960s.

24. North Wingfield, Williamthorpe Colliery, No 2 Pit   SER 1196

Type:	Double cylinder horizontal
Maker & Date:	Markham & Co., Broad Oak Works, Chesterfield, 1904
Photo Taken:	1965
Cylinders:	42in x 7ft 0in. Altered to 38in , 1962 – Cornish Valves
Hp:?	*Rpm:* 30 *Psi:* 130
Service:	Coal winding shaft 1,320ft deep

This was Markhams' early period design, with the valve chests at the sides. Governor-controlled cut-off gear was fitted, which was very useful when coal drawing was heavy. It was later disused as with coal drawn from other shafts, this shaft was less used. In full working, this engine drew 2,000 tons of coal per drawing shift of $7^{1}/_{2}$ hours, making 22 revolutions of the engine per wind, and up to eight tons of coal per trip. Pit use limited 1968, concentrations intended.

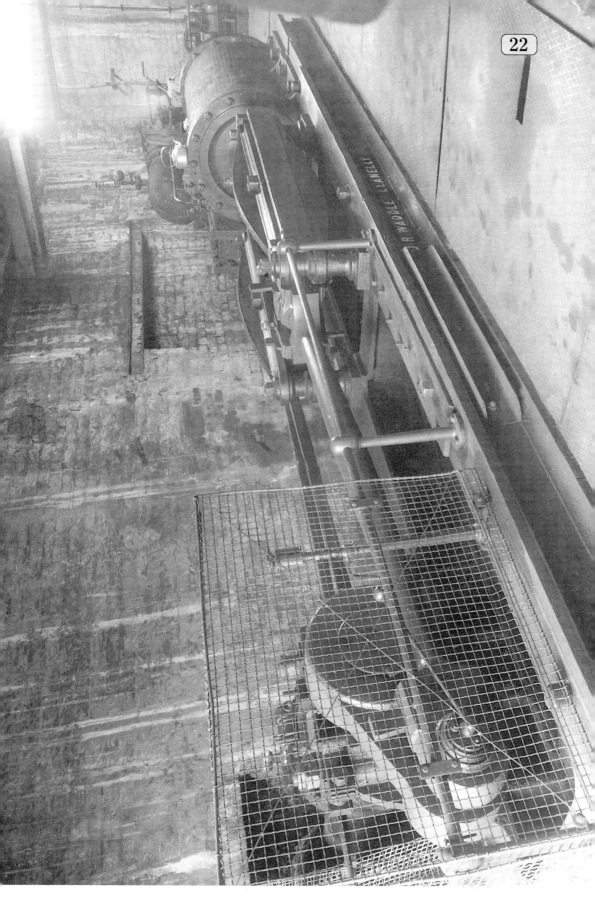

25. Pentrich, Mr Barker, Farm contractor

SER 453a

Type:	Single cylinder traction engine	
Maker & Date:	Tasker & Co, Andover, early 1900s	
Photo Taken:	1952	
Cylinders:		
Hp: abt 6	*Rpm*: 150	*Psi*: 140
Service:	General service to farmers. Owner driving	

This was a typical small contractor's engine, light and handy which with the owner's skilled handling could do almost anything or go anywhere on the local farms. They were used very widely until tractors were developed, and were cheaper than horses as well as more powerful. The owner, seen beside it, had given it every attention, but it was little used after 1948, although the owner did contracts for years after. It was probably preserved afterwards but nothing is known of this.

26. Pinxton, Brookhill Colliery

SER 1370

Type:	Double cylinder horizontal	
Maker & Date:	John Wood & Co, Wigan, 1908	
Photo Taken:	1968	
Cylinders:	36in x 6ft 0in – Piston valves	
Hp:?	*Rpm*: 30	*Psi*: 100
Service:	Coal winding. Shaft 380 yds deep. Rope drum 15ft diameter	

This was a downcast shaft, the pit being connected to other workings acting as upcast and safety shafts to Brookhill. This engine again had been little altered, but piston tail rods in sheaths were added, possibly in the 1920s. Brookhill was mainly a winding shaft for other pits' workings, and heavily worked, had in its day wound up to 1,400 tons of coal per $7^1/_2$ hour shift. It was also a power supply unit, and when fully active had 10 boilers to supply the 500 and 1000kW turbine sets that fed the other pits. The tail rod sheaths were fitted to the rear covers with false flanges and the plain piston valves were 14in diameter. The whole pit system was scrapped in a reorganisation scheme, and the shaft may have been filled in.

27. Pinxton, Pinxton Colliery

SER 190

Type:	Single cylinder vertical	
Maker & Date:	History unknown	
Photo Taken:	1937	
Cylinders:	Sizes unknown	
Hp:	*Rpm*:	*Psi*:
Service:	Shaft winder	

This was used for coal and man-winding for very many years. The colliery was old and the Cornish pump house was dated 1828; the pump was a standby over a century later. The ashlar engine house for the winder, with the parallel motion guides for the cross-head, were early features. Link motion reversing gear was fitted, but the end of the wind and the cage landing was by hand operation of the steam valves.

28. Pleasley, Pleasley Colliery, North Pit   SER 1171

Type:	Double cylinder horizontal
Maker & Date:	The Lilleshall Co, Oakengates, Shropshire, 1887
Photo Taken:	1964
Cylinders:	28in x 6ft 0in – Cornish valves
Hp:?	*Rpm:* 30 *Psi:* 80
Service:	Winding coal from 520 yards deep. Drum 18ft diameter

This was rebuilt by the Lilleshall Co. in the 1920s, with cylinders for higher steam pressure and other alterations that increased the coal-drawing capacity. Allan link motion was fitted and the cut-off was under governor control from Melling's cut-off gear. Metallic packings were fitted to the piston rods many years ago and it was proposed to fit this to the valve rods as well in the 1960s. Fractures developed in the left hand engine bed castings about 1960 and a complete new steel fabricated steel bed was made, which proved very satisfactory. There was a Markham's engine at the South shaft which was 770yds deep, which was fitted originally with a pair of 40in x 60in engines made by Reader's, Nottingham, referred to in *Mechanical World*. [not traced, APW] This was replaced by Markhams in 1921; no reason was known for the change, but it could have been that coal was to be worked from greater depths. The pit had its own power-house, with exhaust steam turbines, but this was scrapped under Nationalisation. The coal was to be worked from a drift in the 1970s, not at the shafts.

29. Shardlow, The Shardlow Malt Extract Co   SER 1426

Type:	Horizontal single cylinder
Maker & Date:	Blair, Campbell and McLean, Glasgow, 1925
Photo Taken:	1971
Cylinders:	12in x 1ft 0in – Slide valve
Hp: 15	*Rpm:* 80 *Psi:* 120
Service:	Vacuum pump for evaporators. Pump tandem to steam cylinder

The plant brewed malt liquor, which was then evaporated to a syrup consistency for medicinal and general purposes in vacuum pans, and the vertical and horizontal pumps extracted the vapour to maintain the vacuum in the pans. It was a simple process but needed accurate control if burning of the extract, or insufficient consistency were not to result. There were also water-circulating pumps, which like the other pumps were made by Blair, Campbells. The site was a very old brewery (1790) which closed in 1920, to be followed by the Malt Extract plant in 1925 with all new equipment. It was latterly a part of the Corn Products Co. of Trafford Park and continued to work until 1972 when it was closed, but could re-open. All of the exhaust steam from the several pumps and the engine was used in the vacuum pans, after passing through an oil separator.

30. Stanton by Dale, Stanton & Staveley Ironworks   SER 1427

Type:	Two inverted vertical triple expansion
Maker & Date:	1 by Glenfield Co., Kilmarnock, 1897
	1 by Glenfield and Kennedy, Kilmarnock, 1902
Photo Taken:	1971
Cylinders:	13in, 21in and 30in x 2ft 0in – Piston and slide valves
Hp?:	*Rpm:* 20 *Psi:* 150
Service:	Works hydraulic power supply. Ram pumps 6^1/$_2$in x 2ft 0in Water pressure: 800 psi

Hydraulic pressure heavy duty engines supplying water for the manipulating systems in the works. There is a single acting ram pump 6^1/$_2$in diameter below each cylinder, with the crosshead and guides above it, and the connecting rod passing down on either side of the

pump barrel, to join into a tee crosshead and crank-pin bearing. There is a single cast iron column at the back, and a forged steel column in the front for each cylinder. The crankshaft is in three sections joined by flanges and the main bearings are set in pedestals cast with the main bed. A small flywheel is fitted at one end, and the condenser is now separate, but there appears to have been a drive for an air pump from the central crosshead. The whole works was to close in 1973-4, including the large furnace and pipe casting units. These two were probably the last triple expansion steam engine driven hydraulic sets at work.

31. Staveley, Staveley Iron & Chemical Co   SER 1038

Type:	Three twin tandem double acting gas engines
Maker & Date:	John Cockerill, Seraing, Belgium, 1924-26
Photo Taken:	1961
Cylinders:	51$^1/_2$in x 4ft 11in for all cylinders
Hp: 7150	*Rpm:* 91$^1/_2$ *Psi:*
Service:	Electricity supply for iron and chemical plant

This plant ran until the works were closed in the 1960s, and there were always two engines at work. Named *Joan, Enid* and *Vera*, they were the makers' Nos. 5824, 5896 and 5897, and each engine weighed 1,000 tons, and its foundation over 5,000 tons. They were very well installed and gave little trouble except for the fractures of piston rods which, a failing with this engine type, was extremely costly to repair since so much dismantling was involved. A piston rod took over six days for six fitters working non-stop to replace. Waste heat boilers were fitted, with superheaters to each engine, and the exhaust gases from each twin engine gave up to 14,000 lbs. of superheated steam per hour at 160 psi, which was used in the turbine driven blast furnace blowers. All of the plant was scrapped when the entire works was closed in the 1960s. As with Appleby-Frodingham, these engines worked very quietly.

32. Staveley, Staveley Iron & Chemical Co   SER 1072

Type:	5 vertical long crosshead single cylinder
Maker & Date:	Galloways, Ltd., Manchester, 1907
Photo Taken:	1962
Cylinders:	36in x 5ft 0in – Piston valves
Hp: 520	*Rpm:* 33 *Psi:* 160
Service:	Blast furnace blowers. 90in then 110in air cylinders 21,500 cubic feet per minute

Four of these were installed new, when the furnaces were altered in 1907 and the fifth was purchased secondhand in 1918. Two Escher-Wyss turbo blowers were installed in 1938, and these blew the furnaces until ironmaking ceased at the plant in the 1960s, when all was closed. There was an extensive electric power station, and latterly the Galloways, when used, exhausted to a mixed pressure turbo generator. There were also two Browett high speed engines. The exhaust steam from four Galloways blowers would produce 3,500 kW in the low pressure turbine. All was scrapped on closure. The demand for electricity was greatly increased later, when electrolysis was used in the chemical plant, and 12,550 kW was generated by one turbine set alone.

33. Wensley, Mill Close Lead Mine   SER 254

Type:	2 Cornish engines (Works No 154 & 170)
Maker & Date:	Thornewill & Warham, Burton-on-Trent, 1857 & 1860
Photo Taken:	1938
Cylinders:	No 154: abt 42in x 9ft 0in No 170: 48in x 10ft 0in
Hp:	*Rpm:* *Psi:*
Service:	Pit pumps

General Cornish cycle engines, these had several small differences in the working gear and parallel motion. No history of the engine was available at the mine, but it is probable that they were purchased new. The placing of two such engines together was rare, and was an indication of how the water load was increasing even in the mid 19th century. Electric pumps were installed in the 1920s, but the beams were maintained as standby.

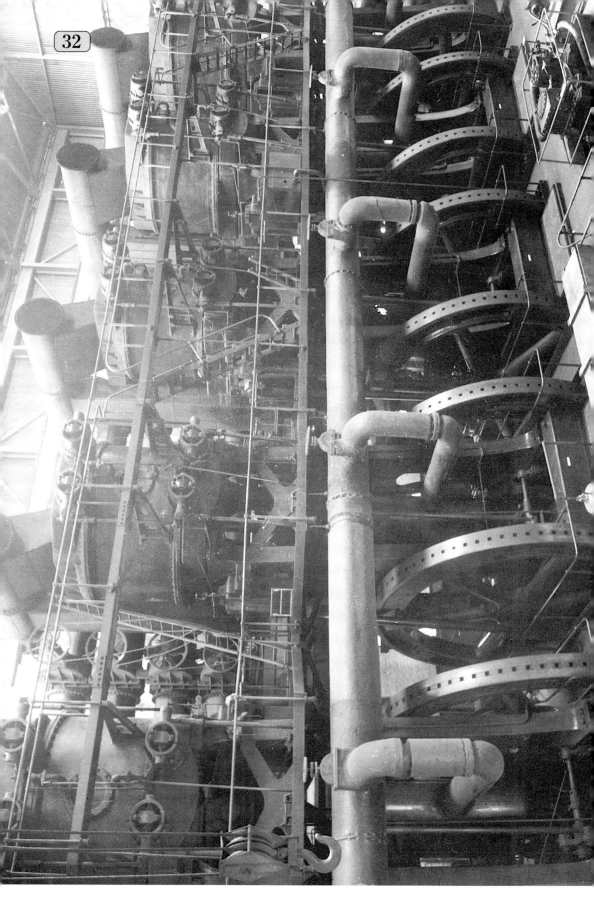

34. *Wirksworth, Middleton Incline, Cromford & High Peak Railway*   SER 22

Type:	Twin condensing beam
Maker & Date:	Butterley Co., 1825
Photo Taken:	1935
Cylinders:	26in x 5ft 0in – Slide valves
Hp:	*Rpm:*up to 30 *Psi:*5-10
Service:	Incline haulage for lime traffic. Geared to cable drums 14ft 0in diameter by gears about 5ft 0in on the crankshaft to 14ft 0in for the rope drum

These engines hauled the railway trucks up from the quarry and when over the top lowered them to the main railway line at Cromford. The engine driving pinion was disengaged to lower the trucks by the brake on the cable drum. This was in regular use until 1952, and until the 1930s still had a Butterley whistle-mouth boiler in situ: this was a primitive type with the fire grate in the front of the boiler with a water casing over the top, and with two flues through the boiler shell. The whole will probably be scrapped with the abandonment of the quarries in 1968.

35. *Woodville, Albion Clay Co.*   *SER 1418*

Type:	High speed compound engines
Maker & Date:	Belliss and Morcom, Birmingham, 1914 onwards
Photo Taken:	1970
Cylinders:	Sizes unknown
*Hp:*up to 400	*Rpm*: 400 *Psi*: 120
Service:	Works electrical power supply

Albion was a very large works, and when all was steam driven with engines for the haulages, clay preparing and brickmaking machines, there were 5 of the 6 boilers in use. About 1914, electrical transmission was adopted for the more remote drives and with D.C. for lighting and power; this was gradually extended to drive all the plant by electric motors. Ultimately there were 5 generating sets, each with a Belliss compound engine, and the photograph shows three of these, each with an engine with differing valve arrangements, and usually three of the engines appear to have been in use at a time. All the exhaust steam was used in the drying kilns, providing power at a low cost, but after 1967, A.C. current from the Grid was adopted, and the engines were then dis-used. The changeover was very expensive, as the large stock of small motors indicates, but it eliminated the maintenance of commutators and brush gear needed in direct current (i.e. D.C.) motors.

Leicestershire

36. *Bagworth, Bagworth Colliery, No 1 Shaft*   *SER 1436*

Type:	Double cylinder horizontal, non-condensing
Maker & Date:	Unknown
Photo Taken:	1972
Cylinder/dimensions:	22in x 3ft 6in – Slide valves
Hp:	*Rpm*: 50 *Psi*: 90
Service:	Coal winding. Shaft 285 yards deep. Rope drum. 10ft diameter

Bagworth had ceased to draw coal by 1970, the coal being worked from a new inclined drift sunk in the 1960s. The steam winders were retained for men and materials until 1973, when they were replaced by electrically driven units, as the steam plant was too expensive with limited loads at long intervals. No. 1 retained the slide valves until the end but No. 2 shaft engine had piston valves fitted possibly in the 1930s. The engines were very well kept to the end. Both were very plain and simple, and possibly made in the county, or Burton-on-Trent, and had certainly been trouble free, during well over 70 years of hard working. In full steam coal producing times, the eight boilers were full loaded, but by the 1960s only two were regularly used at a time.

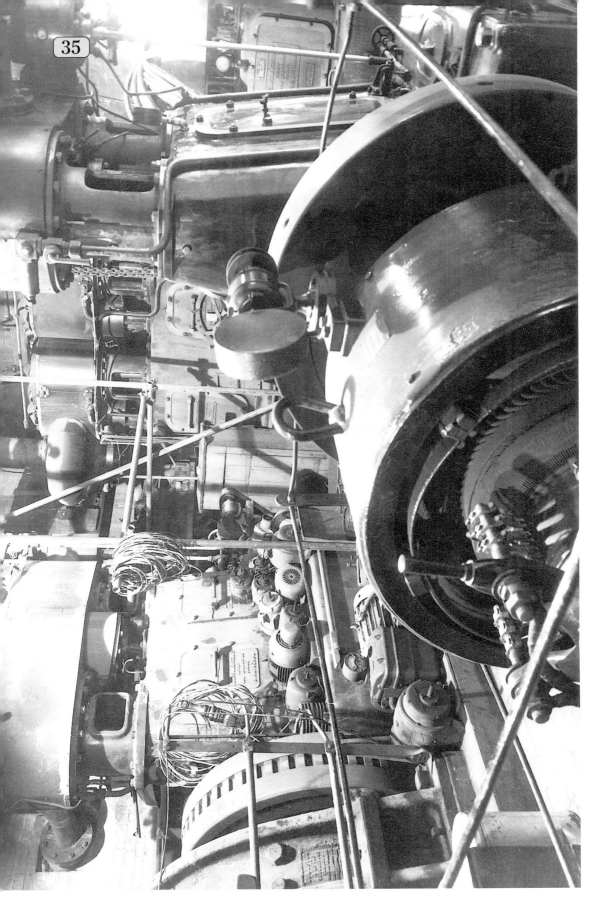

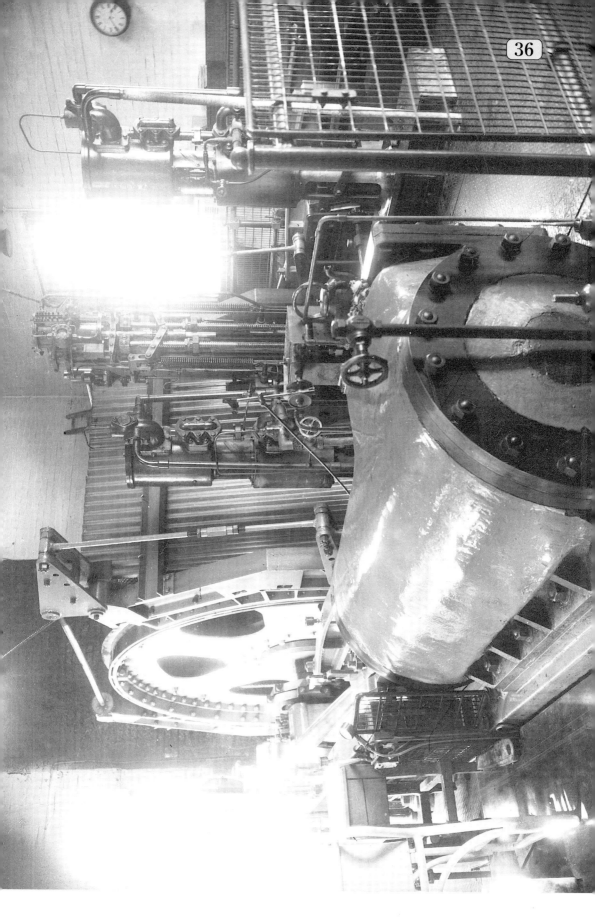

37. Bagworth, Bagworth Colliery   SER 125a

Type:	Cornish beam type
Maker & Date:	Unknown, c. 1820?
Photo Taken:	1936
Cylinder/dimensions:	63in x 8ft 0in. Beam 26ft long
Hp:	*Rpm:* *Psi:*
Service:	Colliery pump. Shaft pumps in three lifts

Nothing was known of the origin of the engine at the colliery in 1936, but in later years the N.C.B. traced it to before 1820, and many design features were very old; it had however, had a change of valve gear, converting it from three to two arbor form. The Gothic ends to the parallel motion rods were an old feature.

38. Bagworth, Bagworth Colliery   SER 125b

Type:	Converted table engine
Maker & Date:	Trowell, Nottingham. Date unknown
Photo Taken:	1936
Cylinder/dimensions:	8in x 9in after conversion – Slide valve
Hp:	*Rpm:* *Psi:*
Service:	Pump rod capstan

This was built as a trunk frame table engine of about 1ft 9in stroke, but was later altered by fitting slide bars below the cylinder with a crosshead and very short connecting rod. The original cylinder was retained however, although the stroke was greatly reduced. The reversing gear was unusual, comprising a separate eccentric and rod for each direction with recesses in the rods, into which the valve spindle lever fitted. The valve spindle rod was jointed so that it could be moved into the required slot, to drive in either direction. The engine was used to raise and lower the pump rod under steam. In mid-position the valve could be hand operated, i.e. not in either notch.

39. Bagworth, Desford Colliery   SER 1437a

Type:	Double cylinder horizontal
Maker & Date:	Wood & Gee, Wigan, c. 1898
Photo Taken:	1972
Cylinder/dimensions:	26in x 4ft 6in – Piston valves
Hp:?	*Rpm:* 30 *Psi:* 100
Service:	Coal winding. Shaft 510ft deep. 4 tons per wind
	Rope drum 10ft diameter

Seen from the drum end, this shows the cast iron rope drum sides with a similar central supporting flange. The new governor can be seen also, but generally there was little alteration in some 70 years of working.

38

40. Bagworth, Desford Colliery, No 1 Shaft   SER 1437b

Type:	Double cylinder horizontal
Maker & Date:	Wood & Gee, Wigan, c. 1898
Photo Taken:	1972
Cylinder/dimensions:	26in x 4ft 6in – Piston valves
Hp:?	*Rpm: 30* *Psi: 100*
Service:	Coal winding. Shaft 510ft deep. 4 tons per wind. Rope drum 10ft diameter

These were almost the last Wood & Gee engines left. It is possible that the cylinders were originally fitted with drop valves but records were indefinite on this. Wood & Gee are interesting in that they gave each side of an engine its own number, so that No 2 shaft's engines were No 1000 and 1001. The design was very plain, with four bar guides, and Stephenson's link motion reversing gear. No 2 engine had a new governor, and there had been alterations in the braking system and overwind prevention attachments, but otherwise little had changed, unless indeed the cylinders had been renewed.

41. Cropston, Leicester Waterworks, Cropston Pumping Station SER 119

Type:	2 Woolf compound rotative beam
Maker & Date:	Neilson & Co., Glasgow, 1870
Photo Taken:	1935
Cylinder/dimensions:	Unknown diameter. LP 6ft 0in stroke – Drop valves
	Beam 20ft 0in long. Flywheel 20ft diameter
Hp:?	*Rpm: 15* *Psi: 30*
Service:	Town supply. One pump per engine, off beam near crank.
	80 gallons per revolution per engine to 135ft head

These were superseded by Easton & Anderson vertical triple expansion engines, but retained. In 1939 when World War II began, they were re-instated as standby sets and the original boilers which had sunk in the settings and were of Low Moor iron, were inspected and, at 70 years old, re-insured for the original 30 psi, and were lifted and reset for service.

42. Donisthorpe, Donisthorpe Colliery, No 1 Shaft   SER 1361a

Type:	Double cylinder horizontal
Maker & Date:	Unknown
Photo Taken:	1968
Cylinder/dimensions:	26in x 4ft 6in – Piston valves
Hp:?	*Rpm: 35* *Psi: 120*
Service:	Coal winding. Shaft 254 yds deep. Rope drum 12ft diameter.
	Up to 4 tons per mine car per wind

Probably of local make, these could have been by Woods of Wigan, the two winders being very similar to each other, and to Wood's design, but No 2 was slightly smaller. The colliery was probably started in the 1890s and the engines had very little alteration or major repairs as far as was known. They were winding up to 280 tons per hour with a single 4 ton mine car, replacing the two deck cages once used. The wind required some $20^{1}/_{2}$ revolutions of the engine, with steam supplied for 12 revolutions only. The engines were very well kept, and brightly painted. One difference was that one engine had Stephenson's, and the others Gooch link motion.

43. Huncote, Mr Bolley's Watermill — SER 320

Type:	Vertical non-condensing single cylinder
Maker & Date:	Unknown, c. 1840?
Photo Taken:	1946
Cylinder/dimensions:	12in x 2ft 0in – Slide valve
	Crankshaft 11ft 6in from floor
Service:	Flour mill auxiliary to undershot waterwheel
	4 pairs of 48in stones, overdriven

The steam engine was disused after the 1870s, but the undershot waterwheel was regularly in use up to 1950. The waterwheel was 15ft 9in diameter x 5ft 6in wide, driving by the usual pit wheel, but the overdrive for the stones was unusual in watermills. The engine drove by a pinion 12in diameter into a gear 10ft 0in diameter on the waterwheel shaft, with a jaw clutch. The Cornish boiler was hand-riveted, with conical headed rivets, but little was known of the mill, which was probably scrapped when the old owner died.

44. Ibstock, Ellistown Colliery — SER 1484a

Type:	Single cylinder horizontal	
Maker & Date:	Fraser & Chalmers, Erith, early 1900s	
Photo Taken:	1975	
Cylinder/dimensions:	18in x 3ft – Corliss valves	
Hp: 90	*Rpm:* 75	*Psi:* 100
Service:	Village water supply	

This was secondhand from another colliery where it probably drove a fan. The pit was sunk in the 1880s and the mining village was supplied with potable water from a spring l50 yards down the shaft. This had to be pumped out and much of it goes to an adjacent clay and earthenware pipe works. The pump, a two throw Gimson set, is driven by the vee-ropes on the right, and then to the cast iron crankshaft through another vee rope drive. An electrically-driven pump in the pit now does this duty, and the engine and pump may be removed.

45. Ibstock, Ellistown Colliery — SER 1484b

Type:	Steam driven fan	
Maker & Date:	The Waddle Patent Fan & Engineering Co., Llanelly	
	Belliss engine	
Photo Taken:	1975	
Cylinder/dimensions:	No data	
Hp: abt 200	*Rpm:* abt 500	*Psi:*
Service:		

This replaced the original fan of an unknown make of the 1880s, and was Waddle's high speed development of their open runner type, introduced in the 1860s. It was used as a standby when the main electrically driven fan was overhauled. Driven by Belliss compound engine No 5381. (possibly 1920?) Despite the small size, such fans were very powerful.

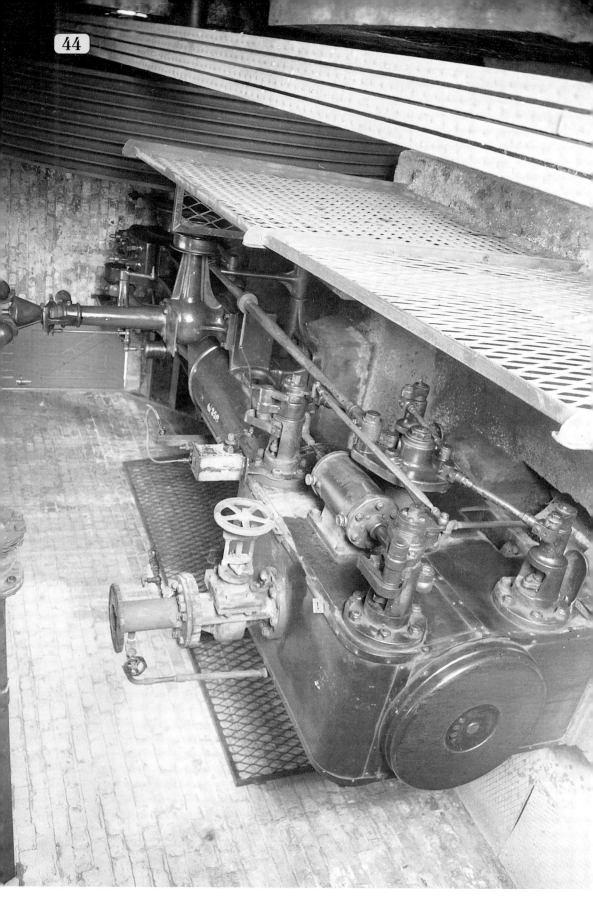

Steam fan house

46. Leicester, Corah & Co, St Margaret's Works — SER 123

Type:	Single cylinder beam
Maker & Date:	Ryde & Co., c. 1860?
Photo Taken:	1936
Cylinder/dimensions:	30in x 5ft 0in – Drop inlet, slide exhaust valves
	Beam 18ft 0in long
Hp:	*Rpm:* *Psi:*
Service:	Hosiery manufacturers. Was gear drives to various points, alternate gears; mortise teeth

This was probably started by Rydes and finished by Gimsons originally. With a growing load it was rebuilt completely, finally carrying three times the original load. A Belliss & Morcom compound engine was installed to provide current for the electric drives, with the exhaust steam used for heating in the dye-house. Even so, the beam was not finished, as it was coupled to an alternator and run to assist in overloads. The cylinder was provided with valves at either side during the rebuilds. It was probably scrapped in 1946.

47. Leicester, Fielding & Johnson — SER 259a

Type:	McNaughted double beam
Maker & Date:	John Petrie & Co., Rochdale, 1861
Photo Taken:	1938
Cylinder/dimensions:	2 x 34in x 6ft 0in – Slide valves
	2 x 24in x 3ft 0in – Piston valves
Hp: 300	*Rpm:* $33^1/_2$ *Psi:* 90
Service:	Hosiery yarn spinning. Gear drives

This was unaltered in 90 years of work, except for the addition of the high pressure cylinders, and retained the cast iron beams and connecting rods, flywheel and gearing. There was also an almost identical single beam engine in the next room, which was installed in 1871, and always called the New Engine. The latter was McNaughted at the same time as the double one, which was christened *Jupiter* and *Juno*. They were typical Petrie design, installed to take steam at 20 psi as simple engines. It is probable that the mill was started to give work to people out of work due to the change from hand-knitting of hose in the area.

48. Leicester, J E Pickard & Co., Oxford Street Mills — SER 763

Type:	Single McNaughted beam
Maker & Date:	John Petrie & Co., Rochdale, c. 1870
Photo Taken:	1955
Cylinder/dimensions:	34in x 6ft 0in and 24in x 3ft 0in – Piston valves
Hp: 400	*Rpm:* 30 *Psi:* 100
Service:	Woollen spinning. Gear drive to floors

This was believed to have been brought from a flour mill at Rochdale in 1870, and ran a single cylinder until 1896. It was then compounded with a Petrie high pressure cylinder fitted with twist piston cut-off valve under governor control, and new boilers for 100 psi replaced the early ones for 30 psi or so. The low pressure cylinder was also a piston valve probably, but there was no record that the low pressure valves had ever been inspected, certainly in over thirty years. The high pressure valve chest was rebored in 1927. The mills were converted to electric motor drives in 1959, and the engine was scrapped.

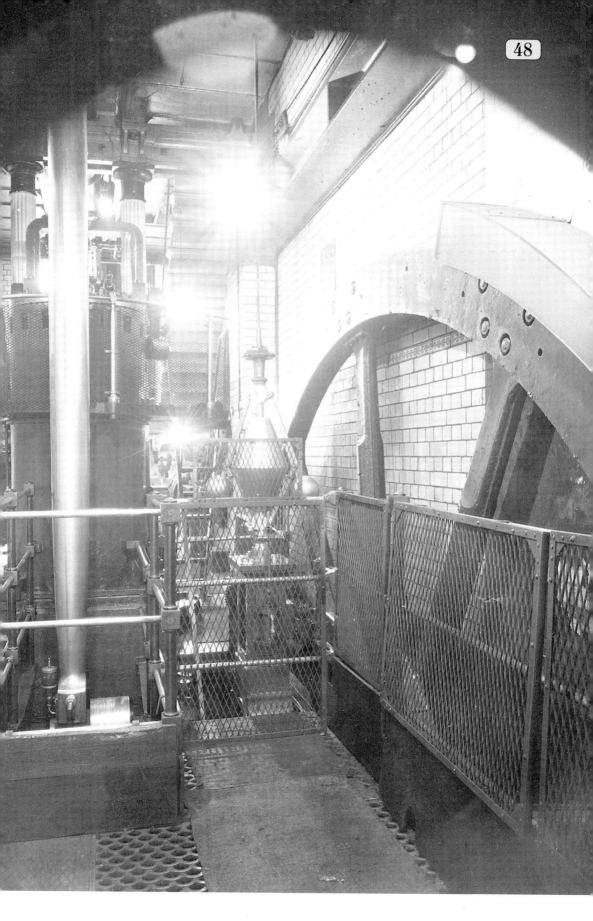

49. Leicester, J E Pickard & Co., Oxford Street Mills   SER 763a

Type:	Inclined shaft to 4 floors
Maker & Date:	No other data
Photo Taken:	1955
Cylinder/dimensions:	
Hp:	*Rpm:* *Psi:*
Service:	Shaft drive to upper floors

The shaft drive to the four floors was unique in that it was inclined by nearly 7ft in the vertical height of 50ft, whereas the usual practice was a vertical shaft. The feature was, however, original to the mill as all of the wall brackets were designed to take the necessary inclination of the pedestals. The shaft started at $6^1/_2$in diameter in the cellar, and was reduced successively to 6in to 5in and then to 4in at the top floor. It was driven directly from the engine crankshaft by bevel wheels raising the inclined shaft speed to 60 rpm. It was fitted with cast iron muff couplings (as seen near ceiling in the print) throughout. The vee belt from the motor to the room shaft can also be seen.

50. Leicester, Leicester Sewage Works, Abbey Pumping Station SER 120

Type:	4 single beam Woolf compound
Maker & Date:	Gimson & Co., Leicester, 1891
Photo Taken:	1935
Cylinder/dimensions:	30in x 5ft $9^1/_2$in and 48in x 8ft 6in – Piston valve to each cylinder with internal cut-off. Flywheel 21ft 0in diameter.
Hp: 200	*Rpm:* 12 *Psi:* 80
Service:	Lift sewage to disposal farm 163ft head. 2 pumps per engine. $27^1/_2$in plunger x 5ft $9^1/_4$in stroke one off beam, and one below the HP cylinder

Probably a unique plant in having four engines side by side in a single engine room. Cylinders and covers steam jacketed, with mahogany lagging except on covers. The use of separate piston valves to each cylinder each with internal cut off valves, was unusual but efficient.

51. Leicester, New Star Brickworks, Thurmaston   SER 1482a

Type:	Horizontal single cylinder non-condensing
Maker & Date:	Gimson & Co. Leicester, c. 1880
Photo Taken:	1975
Cylinder/dimensions:	15in x 2ft 4in – Slide valve
Hp: 75	*Rpm:* 80 *Psi:* 80
Service:	Works drive

This drove the plant, making common bricks, by an 11in belt from a massive 7ft balance wheel on the other side of the wall. The load was very heavy, with a pan grinding mill, grinding and tempering rolls, and an expeller brick making machine. This must have severely taxed the engines' capacity unless the loads were phased not to coincide. There were two Cornish boilers, and a modern automatic boiler, The exhaust steam was used to heat the drying floors. All was in use until it was closed about 1974, the clay-pit filled in and everything scrapped.

52. Leicester, New Star Brickworks, Thurmaston SER 1482b

Type:	Clay tempering rolls, pug mill ands expeller brick former
Maker & Date:	No other data
Photo Taken:	1975
Cylinder/dimensions:	
Hp:	*Rpm:* *Psi:*
Service:	

This was the forming machine for producing green bricks ready for drying. Clay from the pit was delivered to a large pan mill (similar to a mortar mill) and ground to a rough smooth mixture with water and then stored to be fed to this unit. The final processes were passing through the twin sets of tempering rolls which mixed and compacted it to a thick pug which was fed to the expeller mill seen at the left which forced the pug through forming dies into a rectangular brick shape which was then cut with wires to the correct size, ready for drying and firing in the kilns.

53. Leicester, Turner & Co, Bow Bridge Mills SER 122

Type:	McNaughted single beam
Maker & Date:	J. Musgrave & Co., Bolton, 1859
Photo Taken:	1936
Cylinder/dimensions:	LP 26in x 5ft 0in – Drop valve, 1859
	HP 26in x 2ft 0in – Slide valve, 1870
	Beam 16ft long, Flywheel 19ft 0in
Hp: 150	*Rpm:* 25 *Psi:*
Service:	Elastic Manufacturers. Gear drive to two mill and one vertical shafts

Built and McNaughted by Musgraves, this had the main driving gear wheel separate to the flywheel, and staked upon the shaft. Two pinions took the drive for the lower floors main shafts, and the vertical shaft was driven by a pinion meshing into one of these, and bevel wheels. The whole remained almost unaltered until the works were closed and the site cleared.

54. Loughborough, Loughborough College SER 124

Type:	Single cylinder 6 column beam
Maker & Date:	J. Watt & Co., 1850
Photo Taken:	1936
Cylinder/dimensions:	24in x 3ft 0in – Slide valve
Hp: 17.6	*Rpm:* 16-18 *Psi:* 25
Service:	Exhibit only. Ex-Metropolitan Water Board

The Metropolitan Water Boards records state that this was originally installed near to the Lion Brewery in Belvedere Road, London and was moved to Thames Ditton in 1853. It probably supplied a local area by the pump still on the end of the beam, but in later years was used to drive a centrifugal pump for filter bed drainage at Thames Ditton. This required the fitting of a wooden rim for the driving belt; otherwise it is unaltered. The drop expansion valve with a three point cam was largely used by Watts, and this remains together with the pump at the end of the beam; it is in fact virtually as built. One of the two Cornish Boilers is preserved, but this is not an original one.

53

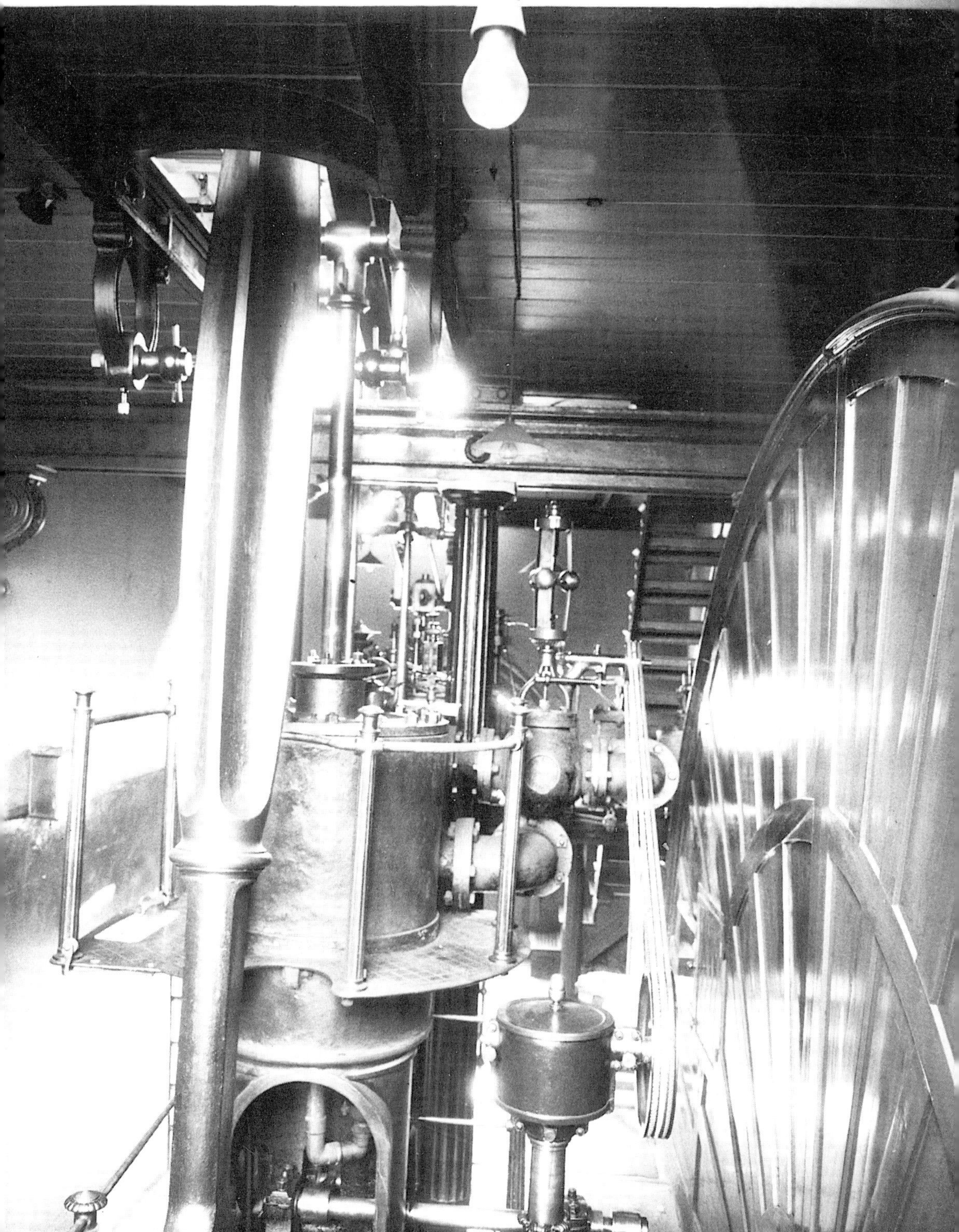

55. Moira, Rawdon Colliery, Shaft No 2   SER 1362

Type:	Double cylinder horizontal
Maker & Date:	Maker unknown, c. 1868. New cylinders by Worsley Mesnes
Photo Taken:	1968
Cylinder/dimensions:	27in x 5ft 0in – Piston valves, was slide valves
Hp:	*Rpm*: 40 *Psi*: 90
Service:	Once coal winding, now men and materials. Shaft 300yds deep. Rope drum 14ft 6in diameter

The engine was almost certainly new at the sinking of the shaft in 1868 (the date on the engine house) but the coal was latterly electrically wound. The engine had been extensively rebuilt, having been built for steam at 60 psi, was raised to 90 psi when the new piston valve cylinders were fitted by the Worsley Mesnes Co in the 1920s. It made up to 80 winds per hour when coal winding, and latterly handled a single mine car only. The left hand engine bed had been replaced. The usual Worsley Mesnes-type of internal piston cut-off valves were not fitted, but the governor was coupled to vary the cut-off through the link reversing motion. There were three cast iron spiders or supporting discs for the winding drum. The wind, of $22^{1}/_{2}$ revolutions, took 35 seconds with steam completely cut-off at the 12th revolution.

56. Nailstone, Nailstone Colliery   SER 1419

Type:	Double cylinder horizontal
Maker & Date:	Worsley Mesnes Co., Wigan, 1921
Photo Taken:	1970
Cylinder/dimensions:	24in x 4ft 0in – Piston valves
Hp:	*Rpm*: 40 *Psi: 80*
Service:	Coal winding. Shaft 170 yds deep. Rope drum 12ft diameter. 2 tons of coal per wind

The colliery was started in the 1880s, but no dates were known, and it was closed in 1970 when all the plant was scrapped. There was only one shaft at the pit, which was connected to another, possibly Bagworth, each providing escape facility for the other. At one time the colliery had worked coal from the 150 as well as the 170 yds. deep seams, and then there were twin drums side by side of 12 and 14 ft diameter to allow simultaneous working of the two depths. The plant was very well kept. It was a pity that with general rearrangements in the area, with a deep drift for gaining the coal from several collieries, Nailstone was closed, and other pits reduced to men and materials duties. There were 6 boilers in use when Nailstone had its own fan and power system.

57. Snarestone, Hinckley Water Works, Snarestone Pumping Station   SER 126

Type:	2 single cylinder beam rotative
Maker & Date:	Bever, Dorling, Dewsbury, 1892
Photo Taken:	1936
Cylinder/dimensions:	24in x 3ft 6in – Drop valves
Hp: 85	*Rpm* 16-20: *Psi: 50*
Service:	Town supply from wells. Built for 12 gallons per stroke, altered to 20 gallons. Wells 120ft deep. Forcing to 200ft to reservoir.

These were built for about 30 hp. each, but the alterations increased this to over 80hp. The engines were not altered except for the pumps, but the steam pressure was increased. Three Cornish boilers by Spurr, Inman for 50 psi were later used two at a time

for one engine, due to the greater load. The boilers and much of the engines were removed but parts still remain in position. The former staff of 6 men is now 2, on part station duty only. The well pumps were at the end of the beams, with the force pump behind the crank.

58. Swannington, Whitwick Colliery Co., Calcutta Pumping Station SER 429

Type:	Horizontal Tandem single crank rotative
Maker & Date:	R. Stephenson & Co., Newcastle-on-Tyne, No 328, 1877
Photo Taken:	1957
Cylinder/dimensions:	42in x 72in x 8ft 0in – Slide valve
Hp: 500?	*Rpm:* 8 then 5 *Psi:* 60
Service:	Colliery pumps

Very large slow speed engine driving the shaft pumps off the low-pressure cylinder tail rod. There were 2 sets of pumps with 26in barrels, pumping from a lodge 90 yards down and driven through bell cranks. It was some 70ft long in the engine bed, and over 120ft from end to end of the engine and pump beds; the flywheel was 32ft diameter. It was steamed by 5 Cornish boilers also by R. Stephenson, 1874. It was replaced by electric submersible pumps in 1947, when a very heavy feeder drowned the shaft, and the engine pump rods had to be removed to make room for the new rising main. All was scrapped in the early 1950s.

Lincolnshire

59. Boston, Messrs Dunmore, Garage Proprietors   SER 516c

Type:	Single cylinder semi-portable
Maker & Date:	Savages, Kings Lynn, No 894, 1922
Photo Taken:	1952
Cylinder/dimensions:	3$^{1}/_{2}$in x 7in – Slide valve
Hp: 54	*Rpm:* 180 *Psi:* 150
Service:	Fairground engine, drove roundabout

This was believed to be the last but one fairground centre engine (as they were called) ever made. They were situated in the centre of the roundabout, which carried numerous wooden horses and other imitation animals upon which the passengers rode, for some five minutes per run, usually at some 16 to 18 turns per minute. Most of the roundabouts were fitted with an organ, usually driven by a separate engine such as that seen at the right, also made by Savages. The engine-men took great pride in their machines, which were undoubtedly the best maintained units in the travelling industry. Fortunately a number are preserved.

60. Boston, Grain Elevators, Boston Docks   SER 1172

Type:	Inverted vertical single cylinder non-condensing
Maker & Date:	S. S. Stott & Co., Haslingden, 1891
Photo Taken:	1964
Cylinder/dimensions:	12in x 1ft 6in – Slide valve
Hp: 50	*Rpm:* 120 *Psi:* 100
Service:	Drove grain elevator systems. Exhaust steam to feed water heater

Stotts were specialists in grain elevating machinery, and supplied most of that at Boston, where the granaries were some 300 feet long, 50 feet wide, and 50 feet high. Stotts made very few vertical engines. This was very heavily loaded, since beside driving the bucket elevator to the top, it also drove the traversing belts to fill each floor as well as a belt conveyor under the quayside to the elevator and granary. The boiler was a large Cochran-type for 100 psi, and the engine was stopped when this was condemned in 1963. Some trouble occurred with electrical drive, and finally a 40 hp motor was installed, which was belted to the engine crankshaft, retaining all of the original drives. The engine thus remains largely intact, as a countershaft.

61. *Boston, Hall, Hill & Co, Railway Sleeper Mills*   SER 1174

Type:	Two Willans compound three crank engines.
Maker & Date:	Willans & Robinson, Nos 2607 and 2899, c. 1890s?
Photo Taken:	1964
Cylinder/dimensions:	Not stated
Hp: About 125	*Rpm*: 450 *Psi*: 120
Service:	Power for sawmill, creosoting plant etc

The plant was originally steamed by 3 Lancashire boilers, but later by 2 ex-railway locomotive boilers of large size. The Willans were supplemented by a Belliss and Morcom "C" type compound engine of 1905. The engines were run condensing, with a Wheeler surface condenser, with provision for atmospheric exhaust as well. The brick chimney was 120 feet high and was a landmark for miles around. The main product was railway track sleepers, fully prepared and creosote pickled, with a wide range of general sawmilling.

62. *Boston, Hydraulic Coal Loading Tips*   SER 1175

Type:	Hydraulic lifting and tipping platform
Maker & Date:	Unknown
Photo Taken:	1964
Cylinder/dimensions:	No other data
Hp:	*Rpm*: *Psi*:
Service:	Loading coal from Thoresby Colliery. Trucks lifted about 18ft high

There were two lines of rails supplying full, and removing the empty, trucks. The latter were run onto the lifting platform which is raised to about 18 ft. high by a ram at either side of the platform. The centre section of the platform is hinged and has rails on which the railway truck is loaded. It also has a single ram beneath, by which one end of the platform can be raised, when at the top of the lift, to tip the coal through the end door of the truck onto the shoot and so down into the vessel's hold. The platform is seen in the print at the top of the lift with the central ram extended to raise the end, and tip the coal on to the shoot. There were six men in the gang, two riding the platform and four working the full and empty trucks around the tip by ropes and hydraulic capstans. A 10 ton truck was emptied in about $2^1/_2$ minutes average.

63. *Boston, Towell & Co, Sawmills, Boston Docks*   SER 1173

Type:	Inverted vertical single cylinder non-condensing
Maker & Date:	John Tickle, Providence Foundry, West Bromwich
Photo Taken:	1964
Cylinder/dimensions:	6ft x 1ft 0in – Slide valves
Hp: 5-6	*Rpm*: 60 *Psi*: 40
Service:	Drive for creosoting plant less vacuum and creosote pressure pumps

This drove the vacuum pump for the creosote chamber (to extract all the air possible from the timber in the chamber, prior to admitting hot creosote) and then pressurising this to force the creosote into the chamber and timber, which absorbed the creosote to about 1 inch depth. It was a very simple and primitive plant, which served its purpose perfectly. The vacuum pump can be seen at the left, working at one half of the engine speed, with the twin ram creosote pumps at the right, near to the creosoting chamber. This remained at work in the late 1960s, as long as creosoting was done. It could be little bettered.

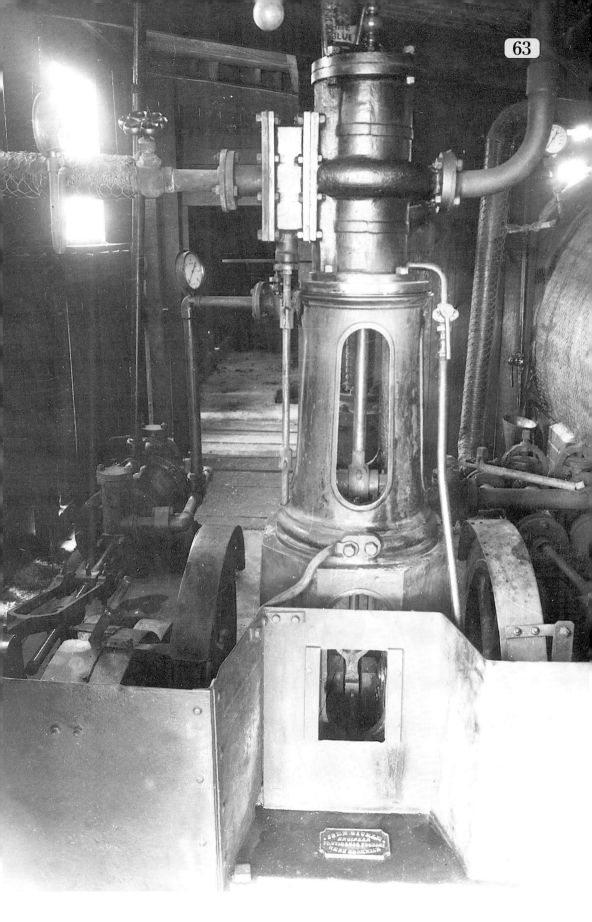

64. Crowle, Belton Brick Co   SER 1502

Type:	Horizontal single cylinder
Maker & Date:	Bradley & Craven
Photo Taken:	1974
Cylinder/dimensions:	13$^1/_2$in x 2ft – Slide valve
Hp: 50	*Rpm:* 100 *Psi: 100*
Service:	Works drive

The works were electrically driven from Grid current and some from a Belliss set No 3027 – 75 kW, and Browett & Lindley No 2711 – both high speed compounds with generator. The Bradley and Craven had once driven the brick-making machine, by a shaft through wall and belts. Very plain engine with cast iron disc crank, 9ft one piece flywheel – soft packed glands – single connecting rod ends. The cylinder was mounted on a single casting bed plate 7ft 3ins long, which had one time had either a condenser or low pressure cylinder behind. It was built with a Meyer cut-off valve, later replaced with a plain "D" valve. One high speed engine was in use to reduce heavy load but the cost of fuel made it too costly and it was intended to go all electric in 1978. The Bradley and Craven was probably stopped in the late 1940s. There were two Lancashire boilers, one a Davy Bros, No 2243 of 1923, – the other had a Galloways supermiser - combined economiser with a super heater fitted.

65. Frithville, nr Boston, Mr R. Crawford   SER 571

Type:	Twin cylinder tractor – overtype
Maker & Date:	Fodens Ltd., Sandbach, Cheshire., 1920s
Photo Taken:	1953
Cylinder/dimensions:	5in x 7in – Poppet valves
Hp: 60	*Rpm:* 300 *Psi: 200*
Service:	General haulage

Probably only three examples of this design were made, the other two being exported. Called the *Sun* tractor, it comprised the power plant of the Foden Speed Six undertype steam wagon, but with the engine mounted as an overtype upon the top of the boiler, with a chain drive to the rear wheels. The engine was a high speed poppet valve-type designed to use highly superheated steam. The boiler was of water tube design with numerous water tubes crossing diagonally in an inclined rectangular flue. This example was preserved by Mr. Crawford and was run during the Foden centenary celebrations.

66. Frithville, nr Boston, Mr R. Crawford   SER 571A

Type:	Foden Sun Tractor
Maker & Date:	
Photo Taken:	1953
Cylinder/dimensions:	
Hp:	*Rpm:* *Psi:*
Service:	At the Foden's Centenary Show

This is the tractor as it was exhibited at the Foden's Centenary meeting at Sandbach, when there were almost every type of Foden's road vehicles shown. The standard design was an undertype wagon, and this was an experimental light tractor design. The two prints indicate the amount of work which was involved in preparing a vehicle for an important rally such as the Centenary one, from the workable to the exhibit state.

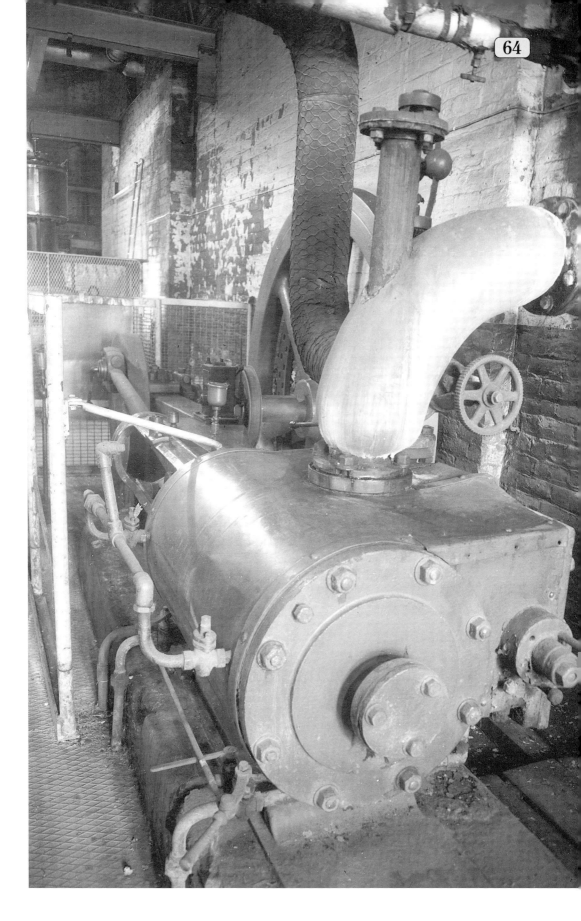

67. Gosberton, Mr Bates, Contractor   SER 572

Type:	Single cylinder roller
Maker & Date:	Thos. Green & Son, Leeds, Date unknown
Photo Taken:	1953
Cylinder/dimensions:	abt 8in x 10in – Slide valve
Hp:	*Rpm:* *Psi:*
Service:	Road rolling

This was the standard Green's roller, with the crankshaft almost over the rear rolling wheels. Two speeds were fitted, the valve gearing was on the offside (it was on the near or left hand as a rule), there were trunk guides for the crosshead, and the crankshaft was bent from a single round bar. It had been much used until steam rolling ceased in the 1950s. A few engines of this type were built as tandem compounds (see SER. 518 about this).

68. Grimsby, Grimsby Waterworks   SER 148a

Type:	6 column Woolf compound beam
Maker & Date:	Easton and Anderson, 1875
Photo Taken:	1936
Cylinder/dimensions:	15in x 3ft 1$^1/_2$in and 25in x 4ft 6in – Slide valves
Hp: 50 (90 actual)	*Rpm:* 29 *Psi:* 75
Service:	Town supply. 2 sets of three-throw gear-driven pumps 12in x 2ft 0in 21rpm. 860,000 gallons per day

This was typical Eastons design, with a Meyer valve on the H.P. cylinder. One unusual feature was that the beam comprised twin rolled plated rivetted together. The contract required that it be finished "in the best style London workmanship". The steam plant was all scrapped c. 1947? The crank pit of this was lined with coloured tiles.

69. Grimsby, Grimsby Waterworks   SER 148b

Type:	A-frame Woolf compound beam
Maker & Date:	J. Watt & Co., 1882
Photo Taken:	1936
Cylinder/dimensions:	HP 20in x 4ft 6in – Rookes piston valve LP 32in x 5ft 6in
Hp:	*Rpm:* 25 *Psi:* 75
Service:	Town supply 2 sets of three-throw pumps. Geared drive. 16in x 2ft 0in

The contract for this, May 1881, specified that Watt & Co be paid 30%. of the price when the drawings were made and the cylinders bored plus 30% more when the engines were erected in the shop, 30%. more when at work, and the final 10% after working 6 months.

Publisher's note: In the collection print 148a is mounted in error on the back of 148b and print 148b is mounted on the back of 148a, They appear correctly in this book.

CYRIL BATES GOSBERTON 305

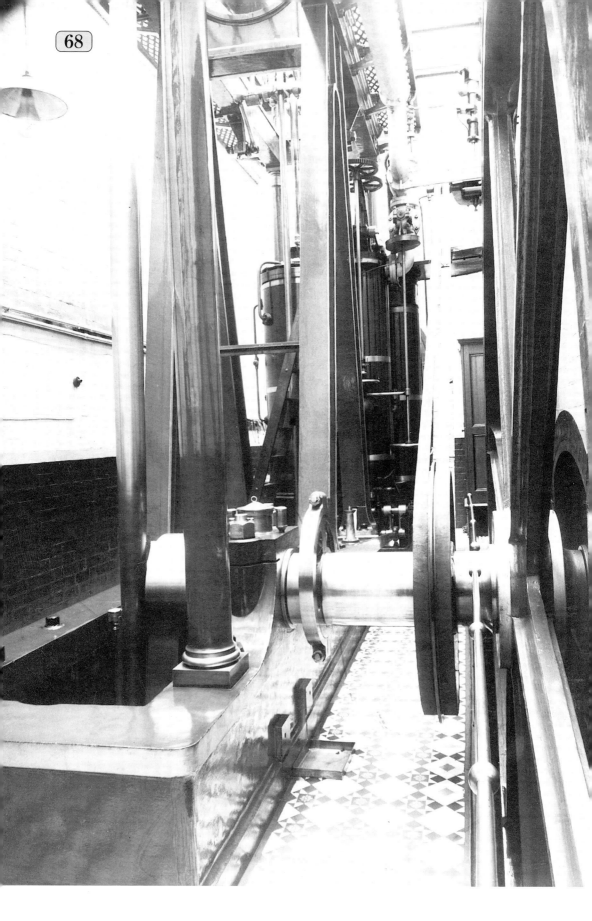

70. Grimsby, Grimsby Waterworks   SER 148c

Type:	Vertical compound
Maker & Date:	J. Watt & Co? Date unknown
Photo Taken:	1936
Cylinder/dimensions:	Sizes unknown – Slide valves
Hp:	*Rpm:* *Psi:*
Service:	Town supply. One set of three-throw pumps. Gear drive. Dimensions unknown

This was a simple plain engine with stiff framing. An unusual design for a waterworks, it was useful here, since it was an otherwise unused space at the end of the engine room and the single set of pumps was similarly housed. The frame design, with gearing bolts cottered in, and steam jacketed cylinders and covers, suggested Watt's design, but no record remained. The gearing had all iron teeth.

71. Grimsby, Sowerby & Co   SER 147

Type:	McNaughted single beam
Maker & Date:	Petrie & Co., Rochdale, 1863
Photo Taken:	1936
Cylinder/dimensions:	20in x 2ft 6in – Piston valve and 33in x 5ft 0in – Slide valve Beam 16ft 6in long. Flywheel 16ft 0in diameter
Hp: 300	*Rpm:* 20 *Psi:* 100
Service:	Oil and seed cake mill. Gear drive to main shaft for crushers and presses

There was only one beam engine supplied to Grimsby in Petrie's records, – to R. Norfolk & Son, 1863, and since this was of 34in bore x 5ft, this seems to be the same one. It was McNaughted by them c. 1903, suggesting that the change of ownership occurred then. It was fitted early on with a drop expansion valve in the main steam pipe and this was retained when it was compounded, suggesting great variations of load. The whole engine and later alterations were purely Petrie's design, with their massive connecting rod, top and bottom valves on the LP, and the twist motion piston valve on the HP cylinders. The mill shaft was driven at half the engine speed by spur gearing, outside of the engine room. Metallic piston rod packing had been fitted, otherwise little was altered.

72. New Bolingbroke, J Rundle, Contractor   SER 516b

Type:	Single cylinder traction
Maker & Date:	Fowell & Co., St Ives, Hunts., 1914
Photo Taken:	1952
Cylinder/dimensions:	8in x 1ft 0in? – Slide valve
Hp:	*Rpm:* *Psi:*
Service:	General farm work

Another standard Fowell engine that had long given good service to the local farmers for threshing, hauling, timber sawing etc. Such engines were the general work horses, and there were many contractors like Mr. Rundle who hired them out as a part of an agricultural engineering business. The wide spread use of tractors has now superseded the hiring system, but with men as plain and simple as the engines, an immense contribution was made to farming. There has, however, developed a massive business in hiring harvesting combines which cut, thresh and bag the grain on the field, and deliver it to the storage silos on the farms, but the steam engines have no part in this.

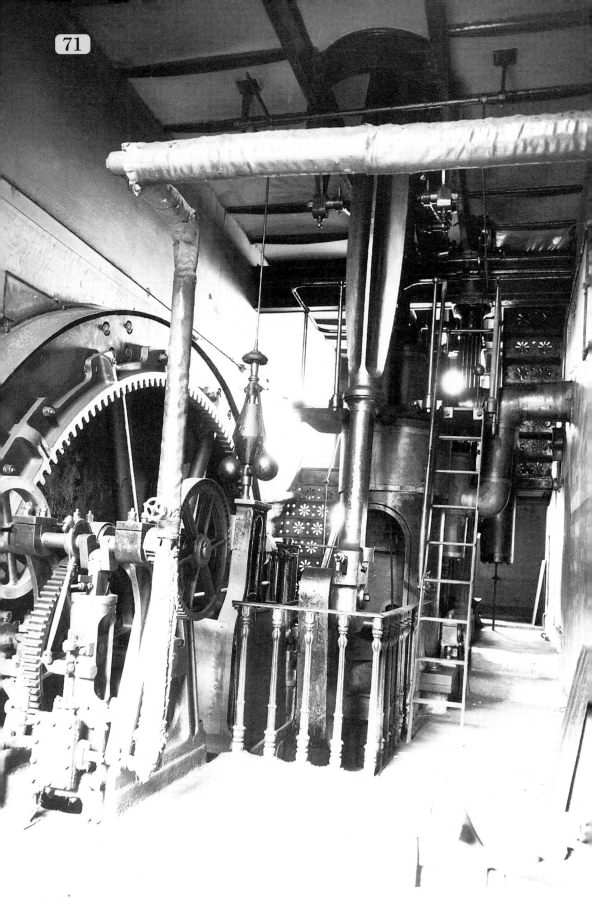

73. Owston Ferry, South Axholme Drainage Board, Owston Ferry Pumping Station SER 1501

Type:	2 horizontal tandem condensing engine and pumps
Maker & Date:	Marshall, Sons & Co., Gainsborough – No 52767, 1910
Photo Taken:	1977
Cylinder/dimensions:	7in and 13in x 1ft 8in – Drop valve
Hp: 100	*Rpm*: 120 *Psi*: 150
Service	Land drainage. 27in centrifugal pumps

The area was undrained until these engines were installed, farming being variable with the weather. They were run regularly as rainfall required until the 1960s, when an oil engine and pump was installed, and one Marshall tandem taken out. The engines were Marshall's standard class L with drop inlet and exhaust valves driven off a side camshaft. They had disc cranks, single, box connecting-rod ends, bored trunks, and soft packed glands. There were two Marshall's Cornish boilers, about 20ft x 6ft with 36in furnaces, Nos 52765-6.

74. Pinchbeck, Pinchbeck Marsh Pumping Station SER 194a

Type:	Single cylinder "A" frame beam
Maker & Date:	Unknown
Photo Taken:	1937
Cylinder/dimensions:	25$\frac{1}{2}$in x 4ft 6in – Slide valves
	Beam 13ft 6in long. Flywheel 19ft 6in diameter
Hp: 25	*Rpm*: 25 *Psi*: 15
Service:	Land drainage scoop wheel

Believed to date from the 1840s, this was an unusual design with arc-shaped ends for the base of the A-frames, with a similar support for the main bearings. The cast iron connecting rod had a neat swell with slight ribs, with slots cast in it for the upper bearing straps, and a foundry big-end. The original slide valve was replaced by a piston valve about 1920, possibly when a new boiler was fitted.

75. Pinchbeck, Pinchbeck Marsh Pumping Station SER 194b

Type:	Scoop wheel
Maker & Date:	Unknown, c. 1833
Photo Taken:	1937
Cylinder/dimensions:	Wheel 22ft 0in diameter. 40 paddles 5ft 0in long x 2ft 3in wide.
Hp:	*Rpm*: *Psi*:
Service:	Land drainage 5,000 acres

This was of unusual construction, in that although the paddles were wide, and of considerable area, there were only single arms to support the rim, which had twin sets of starts to support the paddle blades. The drive was through the axle, with the gear wheel staked on to it, and although the large paddles suggest a rim drive, the existing layout gave very little trouble.

74

76. Scunthorpe, Appleby Frodingham Steel Works   SER 992a

Type:	Inverted vertical quarter crank compound
Maker & Date:	Richardson, Westgarth, Hartlepool No 236, 1904
Photo Taken:	1959
Cylinder/dimensions:	Steam cylinders 42in amd 84in x 5ft 0in – Corliss valves
	Air cylinders 84in and 84in x 5ft 0in
Hp: 1800	*Rpm:* 35 *Psi:* 160
Service:	Blast furnace blowers

This was the American Southwark quarter-crank design in which each air cylinder was fitted with a separate steam cylinder and independent crankshaft, so that in this compound, there was a separate crankshaft for the high pressure side and another for the low pressure side. The type was made under licence by Richardsons for many years. The blast furnaces at this site were dismantled in the 1940s, and these engines were preserved when the rest was dismantled. The flywheels were 18ft. in diameter, and the engines were fitted with a completely independent condensing system. They were large units some 30ft. high, with flywheels about 18ft. diameter, and the entire plant was preserved in the original engine house.

77. Scunthorpe, Appleby Frodingham Steel Works   SER 992b

Type:	Eight gas engines
Maker & Date:	Seven – Vickers Armstrong, 1925. One – M.A.N., 1930
Photo Taken:	1959
Cylinder/dimensions:	Vickers – 43in x 3ft 11in stroke
	M.A.N. – 60in x 5ft in
Hp: 1500 total	*Rpm* 100: *Psi:*
Service:	Blast furnace gas engine driving blowers and generators

The demand for gas had greatly increased over the years, and the entire gas engine plant was due to be scrapped in 1965, since it was 30-40 years old, and heavily used for most of its life. Heavy repairs would be very expensive, not only for the cost of the parts, but also the very high labour costs due to the amount of dismantling involved. The immensely heavy concrete beds were to be dismantled to reduce the floor to ground level, to use the building for storage. The M.A.N. engine was removed first, and the others soon followed. Latterly the gas, originally from furnaces nearby, had to be carried in large overhead mains for something over a mile to the engines from the new furnaces lower in the works area. It was an extremely impressive sight and the engines ran very quietly. It was probably the largest gas-engined power station in Europe in the 1960's.

78. Scunthorpe, Appleby Frodingham Steel Works   SER 992c

Type:	Single crank tandem double acting gas engine
Maker & Date:	Machinen fabrik Augsburg Nürnberg, 1930
Photo Taken:	1959
Cylinder/dimensions	60in x 5ft 0in
Hp: 6,000	*Rpm:* 94 *Psi:*
Service:	Electricity generation

This was one of the latest and largest gas engines in England, if not Europe, and ran very well for over thirty years until the generating plant was stopped entirely and the current taken from the Grid. The size of the unit, which delivered its 6,000 h.p. through a single web crank, can be estimated by the drawing office man beside it, but equally impressive was the quietness of its working, as conversation could be easily carried on close beside the cylinders. It is sad that such a fine plant had to go, but the difficulties of repair can be imagined from the amount of dismantling involved, since the pistons and rods were all water cooled internally, and everything forced-lubricated.

79. Scunthorpe, Richard Thomas & Baldwins Steel Mill   SER 991

Type:	Horizontal three cylinder simple non-condensing
Maker & Date:	Lamberton & Co., Coatbridge, c. 1906?
Photo Taken:	1959
Cylinder/dimensions:	40in x 4ft 6in – Piston valves
Hp: 4,000	*Rpm:* 100 *Psi:* 160
Service:	Steel rolling. Ingots to billet sections

This was the standard Lamberton's design, of which they made at least 12 - 14 from 1901 to 1920 – several for the Lysaght and Richard Thomas groups. The design did not vary, except in cylinder sizes, having the piston valves at the side driven by Allan link motion; they were massive and rarely broke down, although some crankshafts did give trouble. The whole plant was due to be re organised in the 1960's, with electrical driving, and new rolling mills.

80. Scunthorpe, Richard Thomas & Baldwins – J. Whitehead section
SER 991a

Type:	Horizontal single tandem condensing
Maker & Date:	Fullerton, Hodgart & Barclay, Paisley, No 571, 1907
Photo Taken:	1959
Cylinder/dimensions:	32in and 50in x 4ft 0in – Drop and Corliss valves
Hp: 1800	*Rpm:* 80 *Psi:* 160
Service:	Rod rolling mill drive. 56in belt drive to several stands of rolls

This was installed in a mill in Tredegar in the early 1900s and was removed together with the boilers and rolling mill in 1934. Fullertons did not make many rolling mill engines, but this was very good, giving little trouble, although the load was often fully up to capacity. Wide speed variation was provided in the governors, but the most interesting feature was the wide single belt drive which was carried around the pulleys driving the three separate series of rod rolling mills. The engine also drove the initial breaking down roll system, comprising 7 sets of heavy rolls which were geared together. They took the red hot billet at 2in x 2in size, reduced it to about 1in diameter round section which then went into the three series of stands driven from the belt. There was continuous trouble from smoke, largely due to the stupidity of the firemen who, firing the Stirling by hand, fired all together. A motor was to be installed in the early 1960s, but the belt and other drives were to remain.

81. Sleaford, Bass & Co, Maltings   SER 1399

Type:	Two horizontal single tandem compound condensing
Maker & Date:	Robey & Co, Lincoln, c. 1904
Photo Taken:	1970
Cylinder/dimensions:	About 18in and 27in x 2ft 6in – Slide valves
Hp: 150	*Rpm:* 100 *Psi:* 150
Service:	Maltings for the Burton brewery

The two engines were duplicate, each arranged to drive by ropes and clutches to one underground main or second motion shaft. The maltings were an impressive set of eight buildings each about 290ft. long x 65ft. wide, set in a row some 750ft. long, with six floors. The engines were placed, together with the two Danks boilers, in a house between two blocks of four buildings, all of which were connected by a main drive shaft passing along the fronts of the eight maltings. There were also two pumps in the engine room to supply the great quantity of water needed from a shallow well. The shaft was some 50ft. up and the drive was taken from the shaft below the engine room, to the upper one, by a vertical 8-rope drive. The mainshaft started at 6in diameter at the engine room, reducing as it went along the blocks, to provide power for elevating and handling the great amounts of barley and malt. By 1970 the adoption of malt from other sources led to the disuse of the Sleaford maltings which were then let out, but development, with the destruction of the whole seems likely (1973).

82. Spalding, Deeping Fen Drainage, Pode Hole Pumping Station SER 196

Type:	Scoop wheel
Maker & Date:	Possibly James Watt & Co., c. 1925
Photo Taken:	1837
Cylinder/dimensions:	No other data
Hp:	*Rpm:* *Psi:*
Service:	Fen drainage. 30,000 acres by two engines

The Holland and Kesteven engines each drained a section of the Deeping Fen, and with the land sinkage, it was necessary by 1881 to increase the dip of the paddles to allow them to clear the drain, which sank as the land shrank with the drainage. The two engines replaced 44 windmills and effectively drained the areas which the windmills did not. Together, the two engines and scoop wheels could move about 540 tons of water per minute, the equivalent of a quarter-inch of rainfall in 24 hours. The fitting of a curved breast on the inlet, together with other modifications of 1881, greatly increased the capacity and economy of the engines, which were finally replaced by oil engines in 1929, when the boilers were defective.

83. Spalding, Deeping Fen Drainage, Pode Hole Pumping Station SER 196a

Type:	Single cylinder beam. Named *Kesteven* after the district drained
Maker & Date:	Fenton, Murray & Wood, Leeds, 1825
Photo Taken:	1937
Cylinder/dimensions:	45in x 6ft 6in – Slide, later piston, valves
	Scoop wheel 31ft diameter, 5ft wide, 5ft 6in dip
Hp: 60	*Rpm:* 18 *Psi:* 4 later 15
Service:	Land drainage

The two engines were erected at about the same time, and the two cost £17,000 with the scoop wheels. The land levels fell so that the scoop wheels had to be enlarged. When the boilers were worn out, they were replaced by ones for 15 psi, and Watt & Co., fitted new piston valves to the engines, working with higher expansion. This greatly reduced the fuel used despite the increased lift. In a wet season, the two engines used about 1,000 tons of coal, i.e. about 23 acres drained per ton of coal, for the lower areas. Oil engines were installed when the boilers were again defective in 1929.

84. Spalding, Deeping Fen Drainage, Pode Hole Pumping Station SER 196b

Type:	Single cylinder beam. Named *Holland*
Maker & Date:	Butterley Co., 1825
Photo Taken:	1937
Cylinder/dimensions:	44in x 8ft 0in – Slide, later piston valve
	Beam 24ft 2in – Flywheel 24ft 0in
	Scoop wheel was 28ft altered to 31ft 0in diameter x 5ft 0in wide x 6ft 0in deep
Hp: 80	*Rpm:* 16 *Psi:* 4 later 15
Service:	Land drainage. Lifted 160 tons per minute

There were several differences in the design of the two engines, *Holland* having twin beam flitches, whilst the other had one; also *Kesteven* was geared 1 to 4.8, whilst *Holland* was geared to 3.5 of the engine.

85. Spalding, Soames Brewery   SER 195

Type:	Table engine
Maker & Date:	Tuxford & Co, Boston, c. 1840
Photo Taken:	1937
Cylinder/dimensions:	8in x 1ft 4in – Slide valve
	About 7ft 6in to top. Flywheel about 8ft 0in diameter
Hp: 10-12	*Rpm:* 50 *Psi:* 50
Service:	Brewery plant drive

Although not known as such, this was no doubt a Tuxford engine, being identical to that illustrated in Bourne. (*Catechism of the Steam Engine.* APW) The long slide valve, ornate cylinder, table, crank and upper frame all suggest a date in the 1840s and an unaltered Tuxford, which may well have been supplied new to the brewery.

86. Stamford, Messrs Briggs   SER 517

Type:	Single cylinder portable
Maker & Date:	Barrows & Co, Banbury, No 2661
Photo Taken:	1952
Cylinder/dimensions:	about 8in x 1ft 0in – Slide valve
Hp: 15	*Rpm:* 130 *Psi:* 100
Service:	Hired for general farm service

A typical Barrow's engine, this had been hired to farms for many years, and possibly dated from the 1890s. It had remained completely as built, and, although then disused it was sold for preservation. The single bar crosshead guide, bent crankshaft and the cylinder placed forward of the firebox crown were features of Barrow's engines in the 1890s, and they were well liked as sound easy working machines that gave little trouble.

87. Stamford, Melbourn Bros, All Saints Brewery   SER 1398

Type:	Inverted vertical single cylinder non-condensing
Maker & Date:	Marshall, Sons & Co, Gainsborough
Photo Taken:	1970
Cylinder/dimensions:	About 10in x 1ft 0in – Slide valves
Hp: 12	*Rpm:* 100 *Psi:* 80
Service:	Brewery plant drives

The original engine was a vertical single cylinder with the crankshaft on top, and probably dates from 1873, when there were alterations in the plant. The Marshall engine was bought secondhand in c. 1940, and was installed beside the older engine, which was retained to act as a countershaft for the drive of the Marshall. The framing of the earlier one can be seen beside the Marshall which drives upwards by a belt to the pulley, which replaced the crank of the first engine. The engine drives the malt crusher, mashing rousers and elevator, etc., but there are also motor drives. It is a neat piece of engineering adaptation, and the whole is interesting since both of the engines were on the upper floor of the buildings with the foundations carried on steel girder framing. It was still in use in the early 1970s. There is a single Cornish boiler made by Gimsons of Leicester, to which an underfeed stoker was fitted in 1965. The brewing flow was gravity, i.e. from top to bottom; the well pump was motor driven.

88. Tattersall, Dogdyke Pumping Station   SER 146

Type:	Single cylinder A-frame beam
Maker & Date:	Unknown, c. 1850
Photo Taken:	1936
Cylinder/dimensions:	24in x 3ft 6in – Slide valve
	Beam 12ft 0in long. Flywheel 16ft diameter
	Scoop wheel 23ft diameter. Paddles 5ft 6in long, 1ft 3in wide
Hp: 50?	*Rpm*: 18-20 *Psi*: 10
Service:	Land drainage.

The slide valves had been altered, and other work done on this engine. Bradley & Craven's name was on the injection valve plate and since they made beam engines it is likely that they did build this, although the name plate could have been put on at the alterations. There were no features that suggested a maker, but the design was mid-nineteenth century. The upper part of the framing was braced to the wall by a cast iron cruciform strut.

89. Torksey, Torksey Pumping Station   SER 21a

Type:	Single condensing beam
Maker & Date:	Davy Bros, Sheffield, 1850
Photo Taken:	1935
Cylinder/dimensions:	33in x 5ft 0in – Drop valves
	Beam 15ft long. Flywheel 19ft diameter
Hp: 120	*Rpm*: 26 *Psi*: 10
Service:	Land drainage, 13,000 acres

This was very heavily built, and well maintained. Unusual features were that there was a single stairway only to reach the upper parts of the engine. This meant that the packing platform, to reach the upper cylinder glands, was taken from the side of the stairway (it was customary to have a separate short stairway for this). Also the use of drop valves was unusual in the Fens. Due to the risk of damage the scoop wheel had to be stopped during the worst of the floods in 1932, consequently, in 1934, the plant was replaced by two electrically driven pumps from Gwynnes, a 40in – 250 hp –150 tons per minute, and a 30in – 135hp – 75 tons per minute.

90. Torksey, Torksey Pumping Station   SER 21b

Type:	Scoop wheel
Maker & Date:	
Photo Taken:	1935
Cylinder/dimensions:	
Hp:	*Rpm*: *Psi*:
Service:	

The scoop wheel was 34ft 0in outside diameter, with paddles, or ladles about 5ft long by 23in wide. It pumped 40 tons per minute maximum. It was not massive, yet had needed little repair, although one cast iron arm had fractured and been strapped. It was in two castings only, on each side, with the half rim, arms, and hub in one. The pinion on the crankshaft was 2ft, and the gear wheel 10ft 6in diameter, with teeth $13^{1}/_{2}$in wide.

91. West Butterwick, The Windmill   SER 117

Type:	Single cylinder "A" frame beam.
Maker & Date:	Unknown, c. 1850?
Photo Taken:	1935
Cylinder/dimensions:	16in x 3ft 0in – Slide valve – non-condensing.
	Beam 10ft 0in long. Flywheel 12ft 0in diameter
Hp: 20	*Rpm:* 40 *Psi:* 35
Service:	Corn mill. Auxiliary engine to wind-driven flour mill.

Nothing was known of the origin of this engine, which almost entirely of cast iron, was probably a country make. The only recorded date is that of a boiler explosion in 1891, of a Cornish boiler by J. J. Horsfield, (made in 1858, working at 35 psi, 20ft 0in x 5ft 0in diameter) at Coggan Mill, West Butterwick. The existing boiler in 1938 was made by J.J. Horsfield, in 1881 and since the explosion was in 1891, suggests that this was secondhand when put in. The hump-shaped crank was reminiscent of Horsfield, and the miller believed they had worked on it.

92. West Butterwick, West Butterwick Drainage Pumping Station
SER 116

Type:	Twin grasshopper beam
Maker & Date:	Easton & Amos, c. 1855?
Photo Taken:	1935
Cylinder/dimensions:	14$\frac{1}{2}$in x 2ft 1in stroke – Slide valves
Hp:	*Rpm:* *Psi:*
Service:	Land drainage. Drove through bevel gears to pump below

The only known instance of a twin Grasshopper engine driving a single pump. Fitted with Meyer cut-off valves to each cylinder with the main valve driven from below the valve chest, and the cut-off valve driven from the top of the chest. The socket-ended gland bolts were an early feature, in fact the engine was unaltered in all respects.

93. Whaplode, Mr Clark, The Nurseries   SER 573

Type:	Starke's patent valve gear
Maker & Date:	W Foster & Co, Lincoln, date unknown
Photo Taken:	1953
Cylinder/dimensions:	10in x 1ft 0in – Slide valve
Hp:	*Rpm:* *Psi:*
Service:	Farm traction engine

The photograph shows one of the six sets made of Starke's patent reversing gear, in which there was only one eccentric, driven from the crankshaft through four spur gear wheels, two of which were carried in a sliding frame. One pinion was fixed to the crankshaft, and another to the eccentric, the drive being transmitted by the gears in the moving frame. Reversing was effected by sliding the moving frame, which, since one gear was fixed to the crankshaft, moved the two in the sliding frame which rotated, and this moved the one carrying the eccentric, to the correct position for running in reverse.

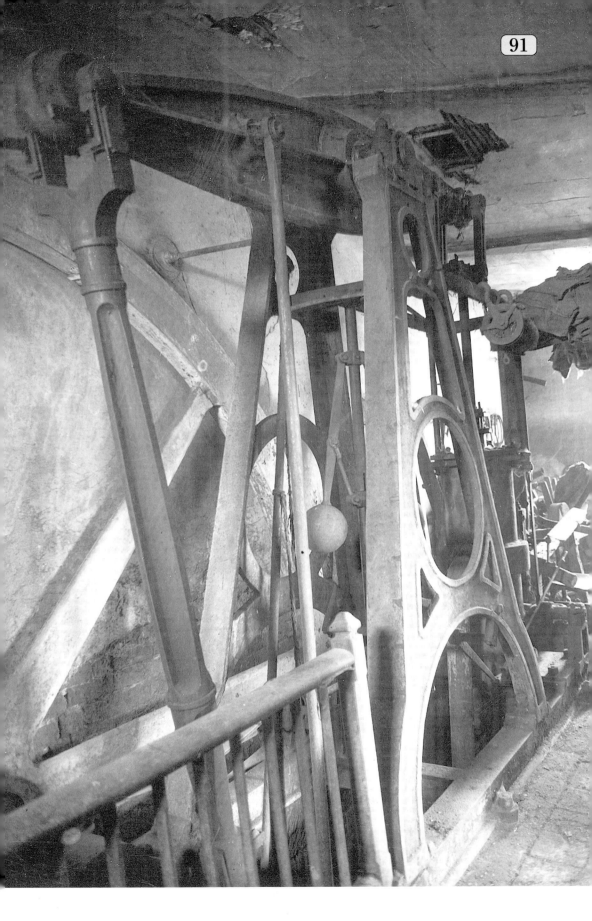

94. Wilsthorp, Peterborough Waterworks, Wilsthorp Pumping Station
SER 145

Type:	2 single cylinder beam
Maker & Date:	W. & J. Galloway, 1880
Photo Taken:	1936
Cylinder/dimensions:	32in x 6ft 0in – Drop valves
Hp: 18	*Rpm*: ? *Psi*: 60
Service:	Town supply from shallow wells. 1 bucket and plunger pump 17^1/$_2$in & 12ft x 3ft stroke. 750,000 gallons per day each to 80-90ft head

These were similar to the Galloway engines at Hornsey (SER 138), but as they were smaller there was no lattice pump rods, and the connecting rods were steel forging. They were under-loaded, and it was soon suggested in 1882, that they be linered down to 22in cylinder bore; this may have been done.

Nottinghamshire

95. Bestwood , Bestwood Colliery
SER 388a

Type:	Vertical twin cylinder non-condensing
Maker & Date:	Worsley Mensnes Co, Wigan, 1875
Photo Taken:	1951
Cylinder/dimensions:	36ft x 6in 0in – Drop valves. Drum 17ft 6in diameter.
Hp: abt 300	*Rpm*: 18 *Psi*: 80
Service:	Coal winding shaft 220 yards deep. 3 tons of coal per wind

The crankshaft was supported by cast iron framing of box section which, carried up from the lower bed and also carried the guide bars. The crankshaft was carried by box section cast iron framing, supporting the main top-cross girder, and carried up from the base of the engine. Diagonal struts were also fitted to give lateral stability. Very little repair was ever needed, despite a long hard life. The coal was later worked from a new drift, the steam winders remaining as standby units for men and materials for several years.

96. Bestwood, Bestwood Colliery, No 2 Shaft
SER 388b

Type:	Horizontal twin cylinder non-condensing
Maker & Date:	Nasmyth, Wilson, Patricroft, Lancs
Photo Taken:	1951
Cylinder/dimensions:	30in x 5ft 0in – Piston valves
Hp:	*Rpm*: *Psi*: 80
Service:	Man winding, was coal drawing. Shaft 1320ft deep

The first Keope single wrap rope winding engine in the U.K. was fitted at Bestwood in 1880, but it was not possible to confirm that this was the engine. The Keope drum needed only a narrow engine bed, whereas this was standard width to take the full width drum winding all of the rope. It probably had Nasmyth's four slide valves at first (see SER 684), but it was certain that new cylinders had been fitted to this engine, as well as tail piston rods. The steam winders remained in use in the late 1960s, although all of the coal was then raised up a drift by new electric haulages as men and materials were still handled in the vertical shafts but it was intended to use electric plant in these later.

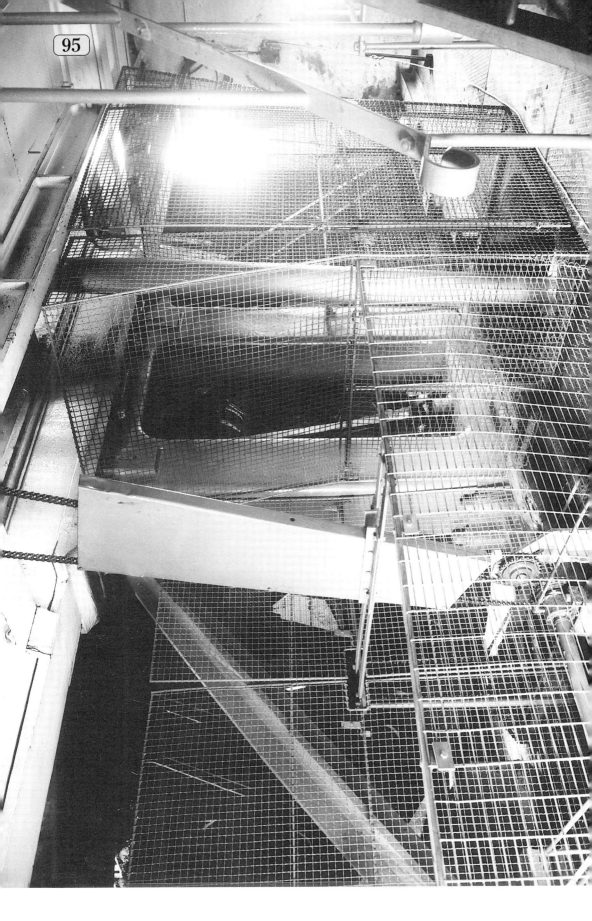

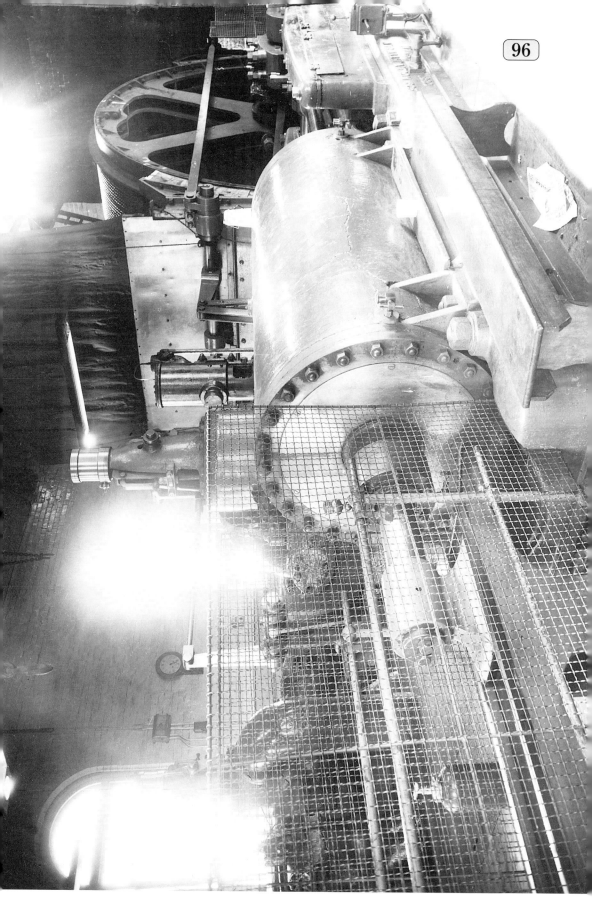

97. Bestwood, Nottingham Water Works, Bestwood Pumping Station
SER 24b

Type:	2 simple beam
Maker & Date:	Joseph Whitham & Co, Leeds, 1873
Photo Taken:	1935
Cylinder/dimensions:	48in x 8ft 0in – Drop valves
	Beams 32ft 0in long. Flywheel 22ft 6in diameter
Hp: 114	*Rpm:* 8¼ *Psi:* 38
Service:	Town supply from wells. 250,000 gallons per day.
	Head about 168ft

The well pumps were at the end the beam beyond the crank with the force pump inside of the crank, and of 7ft 6in stroke. The finish was extremely high, with all of the bright metal parts burnished; in fact it was said that the high finish required by the consulting engineer was so costly that the builders were nearly made bankrupt by it, and these were in fact the last engines they made. They were certainly very costly, and it was unfortunate that the wells never yielded a satisfactory supply for the engines and pumps which cost £14,000

98. Bilsthorpe, Bilsthorpe Colliery, No 2 Shaft
SER 1494a

Type:	Horizontal twin cylinder
Maker & Date:	Thornewill & Warham, 1888
Photo Taken:	1975
Cylinder/dimensions:	32in x 5ft 6in – Drop valves
Hp: abt 500	*Rpm:* 35 *Psi:* 80
Service:	Men and material raising

This was installed when the pit was sunk probably for the Stanton Ironworks Co. in the 1880s, and is still housed in the temporary sinking house largely made of corrugated iron. No expansion gear was fitted, but the tail rods and back slides originally fitted were removed later. An interesting feature is that the vertical sliding pointer depth indicator was still in use in 1976, and but for Mines Acts safety gear it was unaltered. The boilers supplied steam at 175psi, for the turbines and No 1 shaft winder, reduced to 80psi for the No 2 shaft engine.

99. Bilsthorpe, Bilsthorpe Colliery, No 1 Shaft
SER 1494b

Type:	Twin cylinder horizontal
Maker & Date:	Markham & Co, Chesterfield, 1925
Photo Taken:	1975
Cylinder/dimensions:	36in x 7ft 0in – Drop and piston valves
Hp: 900?	*Rpm:* 45 *Psi:* 175
Service:	Coal raising

This was Markham's high speed type with trip cut-off gear on the inlet valves and piston type free exhaust valves. It is a large fast engine which, with a 14ft diameter drum and tail balance rope was raising 7-ton skips, up to 50 per hour. The power station has two mixed pressure turbines by Belliss and Morcom. It is probable that electric power from the Grid will be adopted by 1980.

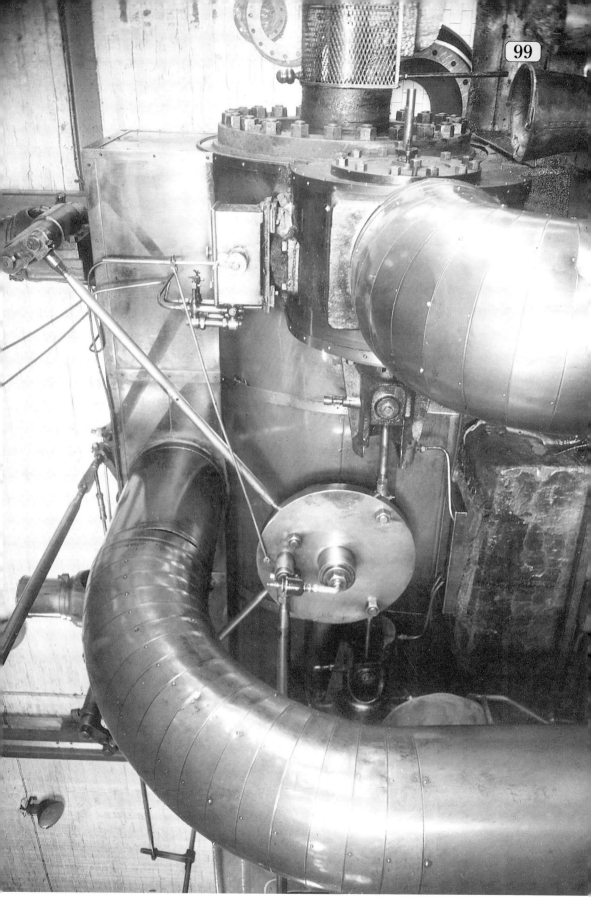

100. Bolsover, Bolsover Colliery   SER 1195

Type:	Double cylinder horizontal
Maker & Date:	Markham & Co, Chesterfield, 1924
Photo Taken:	1965
Cylinder/dimensions:	36in x 6ft 6in – Drop inlet and piston exhaust valves
Hp:?	*Rpm:* 30 *Psi:* 140
Service:	Coal winding. Shaft 620yds deep. 7 tons of coal per wind

This was a late sinking to the deep coal, and the engine probably was the only one fitted at this shaft. There were 6 boilers, and with several collieries in the Bolsover group, the functions of one served another, and the customary complete independence of machinery did not apply. Amalgamation was in hand in the 1960s, and some drift-winding of coal probable. This design of engine, with large piston exhaust valves was very free running, and easy to handle, but the horizontal valves did wear the ports unless well maintained. The cut-off was under governor control, with Markham's usual Gooch link motion reversing gear. This was probably in use in 1972.

101. Boughton, Nottingham Waterworks, Boughton Pumping Station
SER 891a

Type:	Horizontal Davey differential compound
Maker & Date:	Hathorn, Davey & Co, Leeds, late 1870s?
Photo Taken:	1957
Cylinder/dimensions:	Sizes and date unknown
Hp:?	*Spm:* 8-10 *Psi: 100*
Service:	Well supply to surface lifts

Very little was known about this engine, but it was said to have been used in the sinking of the wells at Bestwood and Papplewick pumping stations. At Boughton it operated the well pumps supplying the pumps of the Fairbairn, Lawson engine (SER 819b). The steam cylinders were placed close together, with twin piston rods from the low pressure piston passing beside the high pressure cylinder to the crosshead. The piston stroke was 6 ft, and there were twin pumps in the well, operated from the tee beam at the bottom of the print. The main load in later years was on the Ashton, Frost engines (SER 819c), which were in a separate house. It was curious that in a well documented plant, so little was known of this one engine. All of the Boughton plant was superseded by electrically driven sets by 1973, and much was due to be demolished.

102. Boughton, Nottingham Waterworks, Boughton Pumping Station
SER 891b

Type:	Inverted vertical triple expansion
Maker & Date:	Fairbairn, Lawson, Combe, Barbour. Belfast No 207, 1901
Photo Taken:	1957
Cylinder/dimensions:	15in, 24in and 39in x 3ft 0in – Corliss valves
Hp: abt 200	*Rpm:* 31 *Psi:* 140
Service:	Surface lift to reservoirs. Water supplied by 891a

This pumped the water raised by the Davey engine to the reservoirs, about 2 million gallons per day as a rule. It was said to run very quietly, but using a saturated steam, was less economical than the Ashton Frost engines (SER 891c) which took most of the load in later years. There were three ram pumps to this engine, one under each crank.

103. Boughton, Nottingham Waterworks, Boughton Pumping Station SER 891c

Type:	Two combined vertical and horizontal
Maker & Date:	Ashton, Frost & Co, Blackburn, 1907
Photo Taken:	1957
Cylinder/dimensions:	25in, 41in and 65in x 4ft 0in – Corliss valves
Hp: abt 500?	*Rpm*: 16 *Psi*: 150
Service:	Town supply from wells

This was a very unusual design. The well pumps were behind the horizontal high pressure cylinder and driven by a piston tail rod, with the high pressure piston rod driving to the crankshaft, to which the vertical intermediate and LP cylinders also drove, the surface lift ram pumps being below the crankshaft. The engines were highly economical using superheated steam from their own boilers and the unusual design was said to reduce the cost of the massive engine house. It was certainly an expensive plant to install, but was very reliable and low in fuel costs. The combination of vertical and horizontal was very rare in pumping engines but it was not Manhattan as the horizontal engine did not drive on to the same crankpin as in the Manhattans. Electrically driven plant superseded steam by 1973.

104. Carlton, Gedling Colliery, No 1 Shaft   SER 1367

Type:	Double cylinder horizontal
Maker & Date:	Markham & Co, Chesterfield, 1902
Photo Taken:	1968
Cylinder/dimensions:	32in x 6ft 0in – Corliss valves
Hp:?	*Rpm*: 35 *Psi*: 140
Service:	Coal winding. Shaft 500yds deep. 5 tons coal per wind on 2 decks

Both of the engines were Markhams, but No 2 was slightly larger and both engines were largely rebuilt by the makers in 1965-6, when the piston tail rods were added. No trip cutoff gear was fitted for the Corliss valves, and the engines had Corliss valves when new, one for the sinking in 1890s, and the other when coal winding began. When coal drawing in 1968, the engine was winding 5 tons of coal per trip in a 55 second complete cycle, with two deckings, and making 25 revolutions per wind, with steam full on for 12 revolutions. The engine rooms were very small for the size of the engines. The colliery appeared to have a good life ahead in 1968, there being no amalgamation schemes in mind.

105. Elkesley, Lincoln Waterworks, Elkesley Pumping Station SER 890

Type:	Two inverted vertical triple expansion
Maker & Date:	Ashton, Frost & Co, Blackburn, 1911
Photo Taken:	1957
Cylinder/dimensions:	26in, 45in and 68in x 4ft 0in – Corliss valves
Hp: 300	*Rpm*: 24 *Psi*: 180
Service:	Town supply from wells. Wells 314 feet deep

Better known for their smaller mill engines, Ashton, Frost did build a number of waterworks pumping engines, some of them as at Elkesley, being quite powerful, and highly economical. On acceptance trials in 1911, these used 9.85 lbs. steam per indicated horse power. The engine shown is under overhaul, each regularly running 12 months nonstop. The Ruston & Hornsby Lancashire boilers were small, 28 ft by 7 ft diameter, and another was added to the original three in 1935, probably due to the fall in coal quality. A new electrically driven station was constructed nearby in 1972-3, but it was hoped to preserve one of the steam sets, despite original proposals to demolish the whole of the older plant.

106. Hucknall, Hucknall Old Pit, No 1 shaft   SER 1365

Type:	Double cylinder horizontal
Maker & Date:	Thornewill & Warham, 1862
Photo Taken:	1968
Cylinder/dimensions:	27in x 5ft 0in – Cornish valves
Hp: ?	*Rpm:* 35 *Psi:* 60
Service:	Coal winding. Shaft 275yds deep. Rope drum 13ft diameter

One of the oldest engines in regular use, this had been little altered generally. Up to 1921, even the old-type egg-ended externally fired boilers were in use but they were then replaced by Lancashire boilers, and tail piston rods were added to the engine at the same time. The piston tail rod casings were covers only, but the tail rods were supported by pads near the tail rod glands. The old pit was closing in 1968, as coal drawing was concentrated on the New pit, which was electrically wound, and some 800 yds away. Hucknall was probably one of the earliest pits to use a low pressure turbine in the power system, but it had gone by 1963. The plant was all scrapped at Old Pit on closing.

107. Hucknall, Linby Colliery, No1 Shaft   SER 1364

Type:	Double cylinder horizontal
Maker & Date:	Robey & Co, Lincoln, No 40543, 1924
Photo Taken:	1968
Cylinder/dimensions:	22in x 3ft 6in – Drop valves
Hp: ?	*Rpm:* 50 *Psi: 105*
Service:	Coal winding. Shaft 225yds deep. Rope drum 8ft diameter

Robeys were very fast engines, and this was probably as fast as possible, with the very small rope drum. It made some 80 runs, or winds, per hour with a 4 ton payload of coal per wind, with the governor-controlled steam cut-off in action. It was extremely well kept by first class engine men, and was a very valuable unit, drawing well over 300 tons per hour regularly. Steam was manually shut off at 16 of the 19 revolutions per wind. The coal was good. The No 2 shaft engine was also a Robey, but poorly kept, and used for men and materials only. There were three boilers in use and one standby. There were no low pressure turbines.

108. Kirkby-in-Ashfield, Bentinck Colliery, No 1 Shaft   SER 1368a

Type:	Double cylinder horizontal
Maker & Date:	Warner & Sons, Hanley, Staffs, c. 1890
Photo Taken:	1968
Cylinder/dimensions:	36in x 5ft 0in – Slide valves
Hp: ?	*Rpm:* 25 *Psi:* 100
Service:	Coal winding. Shaft 220yds deep. Rope drum 18ft diameter

Bentinck Colliery had three shafts, each with a steam winder, and once had 16 boilers in use. This engine came from the Brodsworth Main Colliery where it had been used to sink the main drawing shaft. New cylinders, again with slide valves as originally fitted, were installed in 1965-6. Well maintained, the engine had thus given well over sixty years service. The colliery was to be greatly modernised.

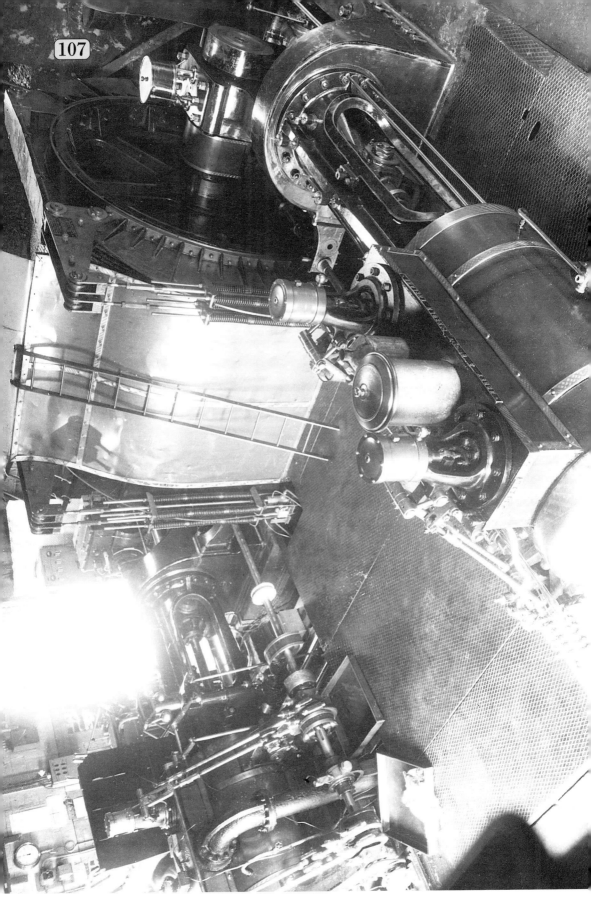

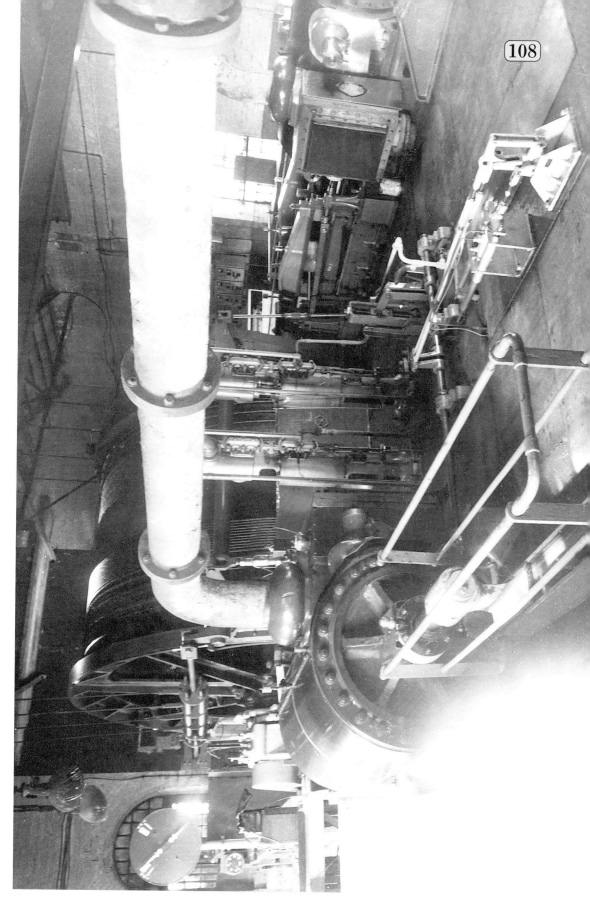

109. *Kirkby-in-Ashfield, Bentinck Colliery, No 2 Shaft*   SER 1368b

Type:	Double cylinder horizontal
Maker & Date:	Robert Daglish & Co, St Helens, 1890
Photo Taken:	1968
Cylinder/dimensions:	30in x 6ft 0in – Cornish valves
Hp: ?	*Rpm:* 25-30 *Psi:* 120
Service:	Coal winding, 440yds deep. Rope drum 13ft diameter

Again very little altered, this engine drew a pay load of $4^1/_2$ tons of coal up to 42 times per hour. It meant rapid handling as there were three decks to the cage, i.e. three movements each time it came to bank. The Y-shaped brackets carrying the valve operating rockers were unusual, as too were the holes in the false covers at the back. A fixed cut-off trip gear with varying setting point was fitted to the inlet valves, but it was manually set, no governor being fitted. As with the other Bentinck engines it was well kept.

110. *Kirkby-in-Ashfield, Bentinck Colliery, No 3 Shaft*   SER 1368c

Type:	Double cylinder horizontal
Maker & Date:	Grange Iron Co, date unknown
Photo Taken:	1968
Cylinder/dimensions:	40in x 6ft 0in – Cornish valves
Hp: ?	*Rpm:* 20? *Psi:* 120
Service:	Coal winding. Shaft 440yds deep. Rope drum 16ft 6in diameter

Very little was known of this engine, which appeared to be later than the other two, but it was equally well kept. The general design did not resemble any make and the crosshead guides were certainly unusual, with the bottom slide bar made with a hollow H-section with recesses cast in. The engine bed was very simple, a plain box section casting, with snugs to retain the cylinder feet. The metallic piston rod packings were added later, otherwise there was little alteration. It was possible that the steam sets would be replaced later, but the main expenditure was underground. When all was steam driven at Bentinck, there were 16 boilers with most of them in use.

111. *Kirkby-in-Ashfield, Kirkby Summit Colliery*   SER 1371a

Type:	Double cylinder horizontal
Maker & Date:	Possibly J Wood, Wigan, 1889
Photo Taken:	1968
Cylinder/dimensions:	24in x 4ft 6in – Piston valves
Hp:	*Rpm:* 25 *Psi:* 100
Service:	Coal winding. South shaft 80yds deep. Rope drum 11ft diameter

The colliery was sunk in 1889, and this always drew from the upper seams, but the North shaft was sunk at the same time to draw also from the 525yd and 600yd deep coal seams as well as the 80yds seams. New cylinders were possibly fitted to accept higher steam pressure later, but there was no known history, and the cylinders did appear to be Worsley Mesnes. The pit was very large at one time having two batteries of 10 and 8 boilers, which supplied the three winders and a large power house with 2 x 1500 and 1 x 3,000 kW turbines. At times supplied electricity to the district as well as the mine. The colliery was to be closed in 1968, almost as a modernisation scheme costing some £4,000,000 was completed. It is however interesting that this expense was mainly on improving underground conditions.

112. Kirkby-in-Ashfield, Kirkby Summit Colliery   SER 1371c

Type:	Double cylinder horizontal
Maker & Date:	Markham & Co. Chesterfield, 1912.
Photo Taken:	1968
Cylinder/dimensions:	36in x 7ft 0in – Drop valves.
Hp: ?	*Rpm*: abt 35 *Psi*: 160
Service:	Coal winding. Deep soft Coal, shaft 517 yds Deep. Sunk 1910-12

This was the last development of the colliery, and it was latterly the main coal shaft winding from 52 to 56 runs per hour with a 6 ton pay load. It was Markham's latest design with drop exhaust as well as drop inlet valves, with tubular tail rod guides with slight pad supports probably. The roomy engine house added to the attractive well kept engine. The closure of the colliery was widely regretted. Nothing appeared to have been added or taken away from the engine: there was in fact nothing superfluous in it.

113. Kirkby-in-Ashfield, Langton Colliery. (No7 & 9 = one shaft)   SER 1369

Type:	Double cylinder horizontal
Maker & Date:	Daglish & Co, St Helens, 1925
Photo Taken:	1968
Cylinder/dimensions:	26in x 5ft 0in – Cornish valves.
Hp: ?	*Rpm*: 40 *Psi*: 110
Service:	Coal winding. Latterly 428yds deep
	Rope drum 12ft diameter. Coal pay load 5 tons

This was almost certainly the last complete engine to leave Daglish's works, as they closed in 1926, and it was probably supplied from stock to the collier. It was a typical late Daglish, with trunk frame, and their patent trip cut-off gear under governor control. The piston tail rods were added some 4 years after it was installed. The pit was first sunk in the 1860s, but under sound management was much enlarged in the 1920s. The original 9 ft diameter shaft was enlarged to 16ft by filling it in and then re-boring and lining it and altering the headgear at the same time. No 8 was always a separate shaft, and latterly had a 1914 Robey-twin engine secondhand from a colliery in South Wales which replaced the original slide valve engine in 1956. The old engine made the wind in 15 revolutions, whereas the Robey, with a small drum, needed nearly 40 revolutions.

114. Misterton, The Soss Drainage Station   SER 46a

Type:	Single condensing beam
Maker & Date:	Booth & Co., Park Ironworks, Sheffield, 1839
Photo Taken:	1936
Cylinder/dimensions:	33$\frac{1}{2}$in x 7ft 0in – Slide valve
	Beam 18ft 0in long, Flywheel 18ft 0in diameter
Hp: 85	*Rpm*: 18 *Psi*: 10
Service:	Land drainage. Scoop wheel

There were two similar plants at Soss, but one of these was replaced by a Gwynne's horizontal engine and pump in the 1890s and this took most of the load in later years. The beam engine was unaltered until it was removed, and was used to help when the floods were high, when the scoop wheel was highly effective with the low head. The slide valves were of the old type, packed at the back, and the whole engine was a model of the time when cast iron was the main material; the wrought iron stays on the flywheel may have been added.

115. Misterton, The Soss Drainage Station   SER 46b

Type:	Scoop wheel
Maker & Date:	
Photo Taken:	1936
Cylinder/dimensions:	
Hp:	*Rpm:* *Psi:*
Service:	34ft 0in diameter. Paddles 4ft 6in long x 2ft 2in wide
	Said to pump 50 tons water per minute

The scoop wheel was massive, with 8 arms on either side. The arms and rim sectors were cast together, probably with two arms per sector, with hoops shrunk on the hubs, and lap joints at the rim. It had needed little repair, although in common with most areas it had, no doubt, been increased in diameter, as the land sunk with drainage. It was driven by cast iron spur gear wheels 4ft 6in and 20ft diameter staked onto the shafts. One scoop wheel was replaced by a Gwynne's centrifugal pump in the 1890s, and the performance makes an interesting comparison. With the scoop wheel, 178,478 cu. ft. per hour were lifted at an engine speed of 18 rpm; and 229,472 cubic feet per hour was lifted at 23 rpm, using 8½ cwt of coal, at a rate of 28,710 cubic feet per cwt.. When the centrifugal pump was fitted to the other similar beam engine, this pumped 97,352 cu. ft. water per cwt of coal.

116. Misterton, The Soss Drainage Station   SER 46c

Type:	Horizontal tandem compound
Maker & Date:	Gwynne & Co., Hammersmith, c. 1890?
Photo Taken:	1936
Cylinder/dimensions:	Sizes unknown
Hp: 100	*Rpm:* 90 *Psi:* 100
Service:	Drove centrifugal pumps directly. Pump 30in suction pipe

This was the standard Gwynne's unit, fitted with their relief pistons to the back of the slide valves to relieve them of the steam load. The engine was plain and very substantial with a slipper guide; there was a Meyer valve on the high pressure cylinder, to vary the cut-off with the load.

117. Misterton, The Soss Drainage Station   SER 46d

Type:	Two engine houses
Maker & Date:	
Photo Taken:	1936
Cylinder/dimensions:	
Hp:	*Rpm:* *Psi:*
Service:	

The engines and plant in these were said to be similar, but the exteriors were completely different. Thus the left hand one is of the later style, giving a smaller building for the boiler and scoop wheel housing, which was less expensive than the other, which was of uniform size to cover the engine, boiler and scoop wheel in one. The chimneys were each fitted with the "cats ears" in the corners of the caps, but it was not known if they were other than decorative effects. Otherwise even the chimneys themselves were different.

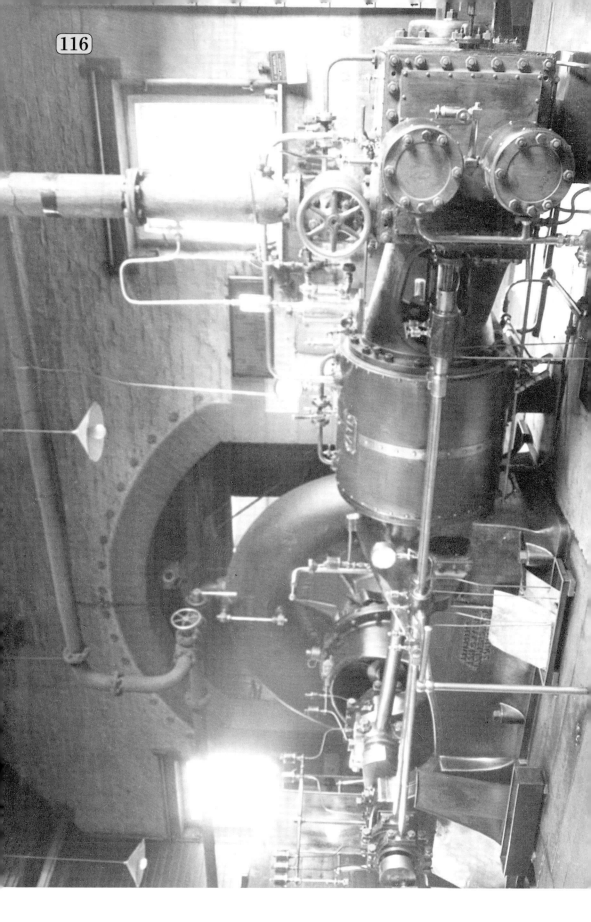

118. Nether Langwith, Langwith Colliery   SER 386

Type:	Twin cylinder vertical non-condensing
Maker & Date:	Unknown, date c. 1870
Photo Taken:	1951
Cylinder/dimensions:	40in x 6ft 0in – Drop valves
Hp: 200	*Rpm*: 18 *Psi: 60-80*
Service:	Coal winding

Cast iron A-frames supported the crankshaft, but the parallel motion beams were of wrought iron or steel. The parallel motion was very slight and had needed repairs. New cylinders had been fitted (with metallic packings) to use higher than the original steam pressure. The exhaust steam was used to drive mixed pressure steam turbines in the power station.

119. Newstead, Annesley Colliery, No 2 Shaft   SER 1372b

Type:	Double cylinder horizontal
Maker & Date:	R. Daglish & Co, St. Helens, date unknown
Photo Taken:	1968
Cylinder/dimensions:	32in x 5ft 0in – Cornish valves.
Hp: ?	*Rpm*: 35 *Psi*: 80
Service:	Coal winding. 640yds deep. Rope drum 15ft diameter

This came from Pilsley Colliery about 1926 and probably replaced a sinking capstan which had sunk for the second shaft. The cylinder bores were reduced from the original 36in to 32in, possibly when it was moved, as the Annesley pressure was higher. It was latterly winding men and materials only. The colliery was modernised later, by fitting 3 mixed-pressure turbines for generating and air compressing. All steamed from four Clarke Woodeson water tube boilers of 1926. The colliery again was well kept, but latterly electrification seemed probable, and by 1968 the Belliss engine and high-speed Waddle fan were standby electrical units, and winding was to follow later. The engine was a standard late Daglish design, with the trunk frame, but the automatic trip cut-off gear had been disconnected. The No 1 shaft winder was Worsley Mesnes drop inlet and Corliss exhaust valves, and latterly was the main coal drawing engine.

120. Nottingham, Cinderhill Colliery   SER 387a

Type:	Single crank. Vertical and horizontal cyinders
Maker & Date:	Unknown, c. 1855
Photo Taken:	1951
Cylinder/dimensions:	Vertical cylinder. Orginally 32in x 5ft 0in - Drop valves
Hp: ?	*Rpm*: 30 *Psi*: 42 originally
Service:	Coal winding. Was 220yd, later sunk to 380yd

The original engine was ornate with Gothic cast iron framing. It was very heavily loaded in 1947, running virtually non-stop, but electric winders were fitted soon after. The engine was certainly well-built as little structural repair had ever been needed despite very hard use later

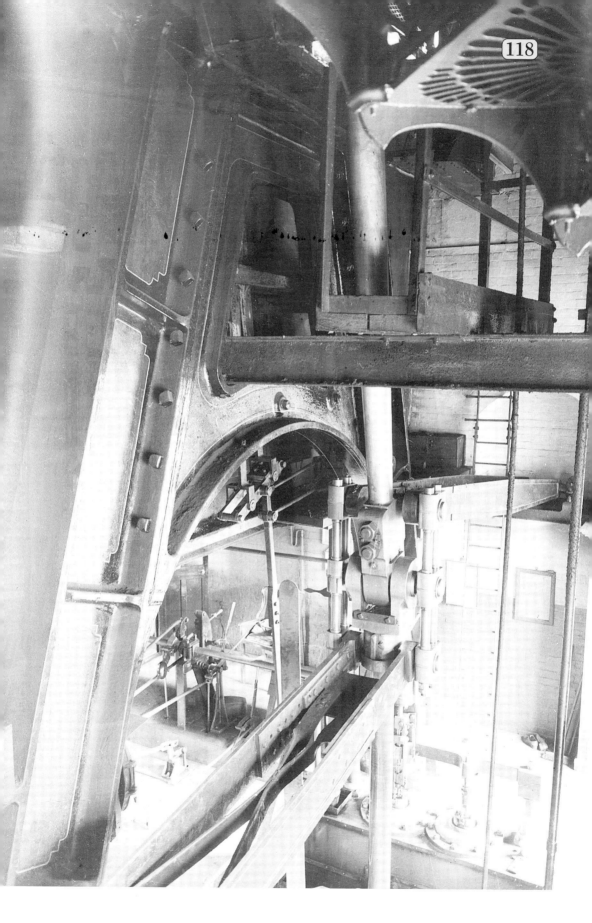

121. Nottingham, Cinderhill Colliery

SER 387b

Type:	Horizontal single cylinder
Maker & Date:	Thornewill & Warham, Burton-on-Trent, c. 1900
Photo Taken:	1951
Cylinder/dimensions:	28in x 5ft 0in – Drop valves
Hp: ?	*Rpm:* 30 *Psi:* 80
Service:	Coal winding. Coupled to same crank to assist SER 387a

This was a complete addition to SER 387a, probably fitted when the shaft was sunk to work the lower coal seams, both engines latterly using steam of higher than the original 42 psi. Both cylinders were fitted with drop valves, driven from link motion driven by a drag link from the engine crank. The engine beds were of stone.

122. Nottingham, Clifton Colliery, No 1 Shaft

SER 1366a

Type:	Double cylinder horizontal
Maker & Date:	Thornewill & Warham, Burton-on-Trent ,1872
Photo Taken:	1968
Cylinder/dimensions:	30in x 5ft 0in – Cornish valves
Hp: ?	*Rpm:* 18-20 *Psi:* 100
Service:	Coal winding. Shaft 265yds deep. Rope drum 17ft diameter

Again very old but little altered, this had, however, had the tail piston rods removed and the glands blanked off; also one cylinder had had a new rear cover fitted. The rope drum was not the original, and no variable steam cut-off control was fitted. The crosshead guides were an early straight topped design higher in the centre than at the ends, i.e. not curved, and there was an arched shaped cross piece over the front end of the guides. The depth indicator again had figures increasing up to meeting point and then going back to zero. The twisted brass casing on the guard rail at the left was an early and unusual feature. The colliery was latterly intended to supply coal to the adjacent Clifton Power Station, but it was to close in 1968, when all would be scrapped. The No 2 engine was also an early one, by Daglish, St. Helens, and, slightly smaller than No 1, made up to 75 winds per hour in the early days. Originally fitted with slide valves, these were later changed to new piston valve chests. With everything steam operated, 10 of the 11 boilers were in use in the 1920s.

123. Nottingham, Lawrence & Co., Furniture Manufacturers, Colwick

SER 734

Type:	Compound Willans
Maker & Date:	Willans & Robinson, Rugby?, No 2683
Photo Taken:	1955
Cylinder/dimensions:	Sizes unknown
Hp: abt 150	*Rpm:* *Psi:*
Service:	Works power plant

The works were electrically driven from the early 1900s, and this had supplied direct current for the motors for over forty years, when a Belliss and Morcom V-type compound engine was added for the growing load. The steam was supplied from boilers fired by waste wood from the mills, the whole working very economically and in regular use in the 1950s. Later re-equipped with A.C. motors, the private plant was probably superseded by current from the Grid by 1960.

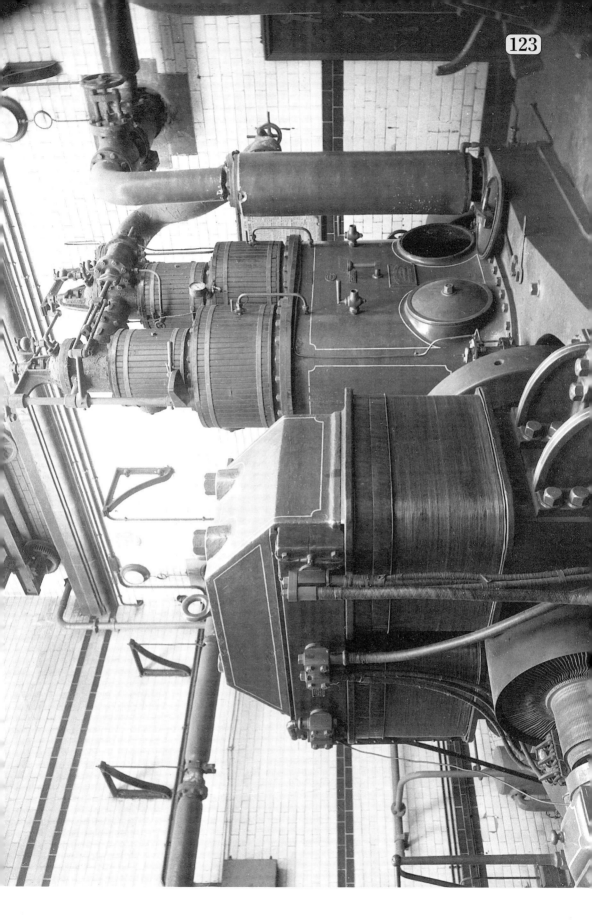

124. Nottingham, Nottingham Water Works, Basford Pumping Station
SER 24a

Type:	2 Woolf compound beam
Maker & Date:	R. & W. Hawthorn, 1858
Photo Taken:	1935
Cylinder/dimensions:	18^1/$_2$in x 4ft 6in and 31^1/$_2$in x 6ft 0in – Drop valves
	Beam 25ft long
Hp: 35	*Rpm*: 12 *Psi*: 30
Service:	Town supply from wells. Well pump 15in x 5ft.
	Force pump 17in x 3ft 8in. Pumped 50,000 gallons per day

There was also a 1869 single cylinder beam engine by Hawks, Crawshay & Co., here. The cylinder was 42in x 7ft 0in developing 55hp. There were 4 Cornish boilers at the Station which were fired for many years by cinders screened from the City refuse. The plant was in constant use until 1938, remaining as a regular standby station until dismantled in c. 1960.

125. Nottingham, Turney Bros, Leather Works   SER 1493

Type:	Inverted vertical single cylinder
Maker & Date:	Tangyes Ltd, Birmingham, c. 1890s?
Photo Taken:	1975
Cylinder/dimensions:	12ins x 1ft – Slide valve
Hp: 30	*Rpm*: 130 *Psi*: 60
Service:	Small unit drive

This drove the petroleum recovery plant in the hide degreasing section, which removed the grease from the raw hides. It had driven overhead shafting by a 10in belt on the flywheel rim, and was replaced in 1975 by a motor in the upper room driving on to the same shafting. It shows the fine craftsmanship of a large manufactory, with the colums and bed a single casting 3ft square and 5ft 9in high, and a crankshaft made from a single round bar. It was in fine condition at some 80 years age.

126. Nottingham, Wright & Dobson Ltd, Alfred Street North SER 42

Type:	Single cylinder beam, non-condensing
Maker & Date:	Benjamin Hick & Son, Bolton, 1853
Photo Taken:	1936
Cylinder/dimensions:	24in x 3ft 6in – Slide valve
	Beam 12ft long. Flywheel 14ft diameter
Hp: 100	*Rpm*: 33 *Psi*: 60
Service:	Room and power factory
	Floor shafts driven from a vertical shaft and bevel gears

This was an unusual design in that there were four columns to support the beam centre bearings with a heavy entablature supported by two more columns behind the cylinder. This made a very rigid frame which despite heavy loading in later years gave very little trouble. The exhaust steam was used for heating and processes, which was a part of the service provided to the tenants, many of whom rented a single room with all service in the rental. The vertical shaft was driven by a bevel wheel 4ft 6in diameter on the crankshaft with mortise teeth and a cast iron wheel 3ft 0in diameter on the vertical shaft. There was no spur gearing, and the whole ran very well.

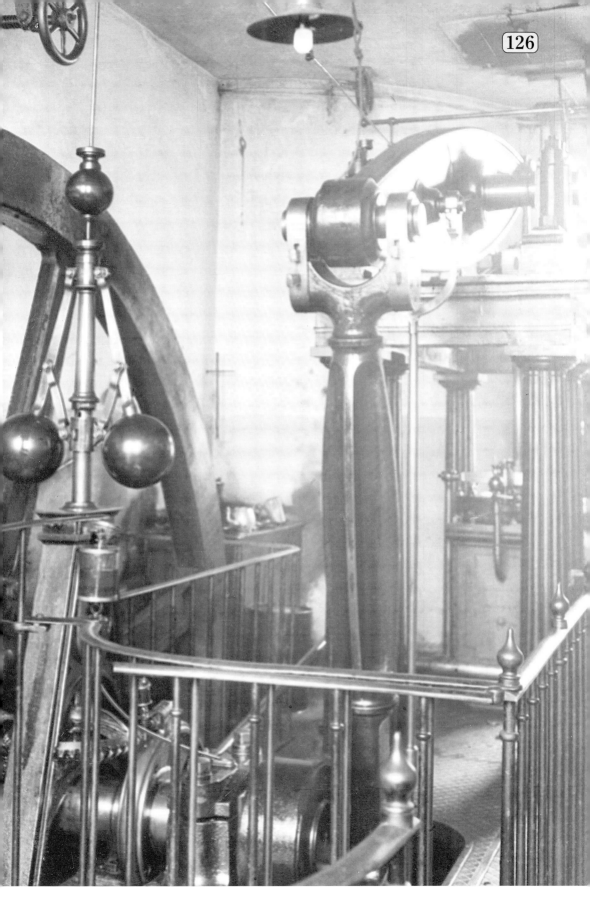

127. Papplewick, Nottingham Water Works, Papplewick Pumping Station   SER 24c

Type:	2 Simple beam
Maker & Date:	J. Watt & Co., 1884
Photo Taken:	1935
Cylinder/dimensions:	46in x 7ft 6in – Drop valves
Hp: ?	*Rpm:* 8-9 *Psi:* 50
Service:	Town supply from wells. 1,500,000 gallons per day each. 250ft head well pumps $21^5/_8$in x 7ft 6in. Force pumps 27in x 3ft 9in

This, too, was a very highly finished plant and the Nottingham City plants were maintained in the highest tradition of municipal pride. Very little was allowed to go wrong, resulting in the greatest reliability. The change to electrically-driven plant in the 1960s was inevitable, but until they had to be superseded, they were exceptional plants. The load growth in the later years had led to wells being sunk farther out, and at Burton Joyce or Boughton there were highly economical triple expansion engines.

128. Rainworth, Mansfield Waterworks, Rainworth Pumping Station SER 118

Type:	2 Rotative Woolf A – frame beam
Maker & Date:	Easton, Anderson & Goolden,1894
Photo Taken:	1935
Cylinder/dimensions:	16in x 2ft 8in and 23in x 4ft 0in – Slide valves
Hp: 70	*Rpm:* 23-4 *Psi:* 100
Service:	Town supply from well. One bucket and plunger pump to each engine in central well 35,000 gallons per hour per engine to 325ft head

Easton's late plain design, completely devoid of ornament, except stiffening ribs. Steam jackets on cylinders and covers. These, together with two similar ones for Pontefract, were said to be the last beam engines made by Eastons. The pumps were at the end of the beams working into a central well, with the connecting rods working in a swelled loop in the single web beam. The beam centre bearings were in sockets cast in the top of the A - frames, i.e. not separate and bolted on as usual.

129. Sutton Bonington, Hathernware Ceramics   SER 1483

Type:	Inverted vertical high speed compound and generator
Maker & Date:	Belliss & Morcom, Birmingham, Late 1920s
Photo Taken:	1975
Cylinder/dimensions:	Sizes unknown – Piston valves
Hp: 300	*Rpm:* 428 *Psi:* 120
Service:	Overload reduction in works service

This is an old established concern which produced ceramic specialties for the chemical industry. Everything was driven electrically, largely by Grid current, the engine being used mainly to reduce the Grid load when a 100hp motor was in use in the processing plant. Usage was frequent, and the exhaust steam was passed to the drying kilns which drew steam from the Lancashire boiler. It was very well kept, the photograph indicating the everyday conditions.

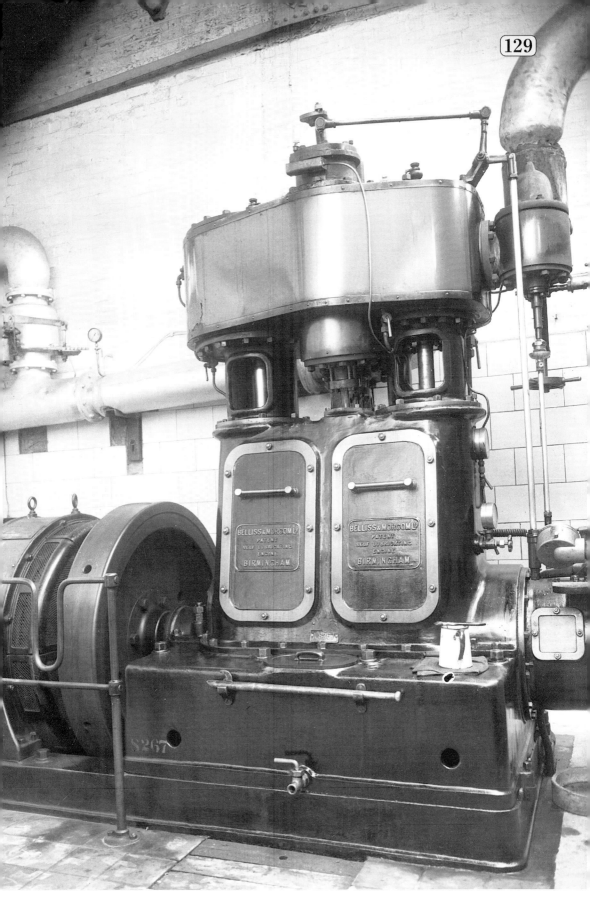

Staffordshire

130. Aldridge, Aldridge Brick & Tile Co, Walsall Wood   SER 436a

Type: Non-condensing single beam
Maker & Date: Wm. Harvey & Co, Wolverhampton, date unknown
Photo Taken: 1952
Cylinder/dimensions: 30in x 5ft 0in – Slide valve
Hp: 80?   *Rpm:* 25   *Psi:* 60-80
Service: Drove brickmaking plant

This drove one section of the works which contained a top and lower breaker roll lay-out, as well as a pug mill which consolidated the clay ready for moulding. The timber connecting rod, heavy flywheel and plain build was typical of Midlands plant. The exhaust steam was used for drying the green bricks in the stock house, and the works closed in the early 1970s.

131. Aldridge, Aldridge Brick & Tile Co, Walsall Wood   SER 436b

Type: Horizontal single cylinder non-condensing
Maker & Date: Maker and date unknown, c. 1870s?
Photo Taken: 1952
Cylinder/dimensions: 22in x 3ft 0in – Slide valve
Hp: 60   *Rpm:* 60-70   *Psi:* 60-80
Service: Similar duty to 436a (see above)

Another plain but substantial engine almost certainly of local make. Provision for a drive from either side of the engine bed suggests that it was a stock design, and the placing of the slide valve on top of the cylinder was an old feature. The flywheel was possibly later and the Pickering governor, too, may have been a late addition. This also exhausted to the drying room floors, drying the bricks from the moulding machines (in this state the bricks were termed green). An interesting feature was that the steam supply to the engine could be controlled from the machinery room next to the engine room.

132. Amblecote, J. Hall & Co   SER 437

Type: Non-condensing single cylinder beam
Maker & Date: Maker unknown, c. 1830s?
Photo Taken: 1952
Cylinder/dimensions: abt 8in x 2ft 0in? – Slide valve
Hp: 5-6   *Rpm:* 20   *Psi:* 30-40
Service: Drove chaff cutter

This is a very old example of the six column design, now preserved in the Science Museum, Newhall St., Birmingham. It may have been a small colliery winding engine once, and throughout its long life (it was certainly in use at 125 years old) had re-mained unaltered unless possibly it had a condenser at one time. It was certainly one of the smallest beam engines in everyday use, and was steamed by an externally-fired boiler in a brick setting at the right hand corner of the photograph. The open lattice-type bed, and general slight structure were typical of early design for small powers, but usually Midlands design was more massive.

133. Bilston, Sir Alfred Hickman, Spring Vale   SER 476

Type:	Direct acting beam
Maker & Date:	Unknown, c. 1850
Photo Taken:	1952
Cylinder/dimensions:	Steam cylinder abt 40in x 10ft – Drop valves
	Air cylinder abt 100in x 10ft 0in
Hp:	*Rpm:* *Psi:*
Service:	Blast furnace blower. Long disused

A typical large non-rotative unit, which had probably been for many years a standby only to the large vertical Lilleshall compound engine fitted in 1896. Each engine was large as the works were extensive with several blast furnaces. The beam engine house was 50ft long, and some 60ft high, but was very unsafe by 1950 and all went in a works reorganisation in the 1950s. The beam engine stood over 30ft to the top of the beam, and the Lilleshall vertical was over 40ft high.

134. Brierley Hill, Earl of Dudley, Round Oak Ironworks   SER 438

Type:	Direct acting beam, non-rotative
Maker & Date:	Uncertain, c. 1850s
Photo Taken:	1952
Cylinder/dimensions:	49in (steam) and 100in (air cylinder) x 8ft 0in
Hp:	*Spm:* 20 double strokes *Psi:* 50-60
Service:	Blast furnace blower

This was rebuilt in 1870 when possibly it was installed here from another works. This was of a primitive type, taking steam all through the stroke, and the companion engine, still used (made at the works in 1870) was very noisy, yet worked for many months on end non-stop. The E-D cast on the floor plates and the plate on the plug rod steady-bearing suggest that it was made at the large ironworks workshops, but local tradition thought it was secondhand to the works. The furnaces were open topped and there was a beam engine to wind the furnace loading or burden up the incline to the top platform. A vertical blower by the Lilleshall Co. was added later, of the usual design with steam cylinders at the top. It was scrapped in the late 1950s.

135. Brierley Hill, Harts Hill Ironworks   SER 247

Type:	Single condensing beam
Maker & Date:	Holcroft & Co., ? 1856?
Photo Taken:	1938
Cylinder/dimensions:	48in x 8ft 0in – Drop Valves
Hp: 600	*Rpm:* 18 *Psi:* 40-60
Service:	Blast furnace blower

This was the typical Black Country layout in which the engine drove first to a higher speed shaft on which the flywheel was mounted, and from which the mill or finished rolls train was driven directly. The forge or roughing roll were driven by reduction gearing from the mill shaft, so gaining the impetus from the high speed of the flywheel, which carried the overload when both sets of rolls were working at the same time. Everything was extremely massive, the result of sheer experience of failures in working. The wrought iron trade was discontinued in the 1950s when it became impossible to get puddlers as the older men retired.

134

136. Brindley Heath, South Staffs Waterworks, Moors Gorse Pumping Station   SER 252

Type:	2 Cornish beam
Maker & Date:	J. Watt & Co., 1875
Photo Taken:	1938
Cylinder/dimensions:	65in x 10ft
Hp: ?	*Spm:* 6-10 *Psi:* 15
Service:	Town supply from wells. Pumps 21in x 9ft 0in

The surface lift, or force pumps were driven by the beams in the usual manner, and the well pumps which were behind the engine house, were driven by back beams and links from near the crosshead, the cylinders being between the two lever walls. The high finish was characteristic of Watt's later work, equalling that of Cornwall. The engine remained *in situ*, but the chimney and boilers were removed. The beams, and in fact, most of the engines were of cast iron. The crossheads were held by Cornish type 'C' collars.

137. Brindley Heath, South Staffs Waterworks, Moors Gorse Pumping Station   SER 252a

Type:	Engine and boiler houses
Maker & Date:	
Photo Taken:	1938
Cylinder/dimensions:	
Hp:	*Rpm:* *Psi:*
Service:	

Another example of the use of local materials in construction, there was no stone even in the arches over the apertures and much of the chimney cap was brick, with Staffordshire tiles for the roof. The result was a harmonious complex natural to the surroundings in contrast to the later "foreign" red brick.

138. Brownhills, Potters Clay & Coal Co   SER 1359a

Type:	Horizontal single cylinder non-condensing
Maker & Date:	Tangyes, Birmingham, 1880s
Photo Taken:	1968
Cylinder/dimensions:	20in x 3ft 0in – Slide valve
Hp: abt 100	*Rpm:* 85 *Psi:* 120
Service:	Works drive by 6in and $10^1/_2$in belts

The works produced very high grade clay, almost without grit and used for artists' modelling and some medicinal purposes. It was mined on the site, and the engine drove the preparation plant, grinding, watering and mixing, pressing and finally drying the clay with the exhaust steam from the engine. The power side was very simple, with belt drives to the mainshafts, and belt drives to the machines with very little motor power. There were two boilers, both secondhand, fired with sludge oil waste by a very simple home made steam atomising burner. The prepared clay was packed in tubular plastic containers, and was sent all over the world, a great tribute to a small plant where everything was the simplest. Even the chimney consisted of an old metal boiler flue. The plant was kept as well as a clay plant could be in 1972, with the mud everywhere!

139. Burslem, Burgess & Leigh, Middleport Pottery   SER 1479a

Type:	Single cylinder- horizontal – non condensing
Maker & Date	Wm Boulton engineer Burselm, 1888
Photo Taken:	1975
Cylinder/dimensions:	18in x 3ft 3in – Slide valve
Hp: 100	*Rpm:* 75 *Psi: 80*
Service:	Works drive

The engine was supplied new to the works when the business started in 1888, with much other plant by Wm Boulton. It has run the preparation plant ever since. Plain and simple it needed little repair. It is a typical sound industrial engine mounted upon a bed 19ft long, with a heavy 12ft diameter flywheel. The single slipper guide is interesting, but it is simply a sturdy and very good servant. The exhaust steam heated the drying room floor.

140. Burslem, Burgess & Leigh, Middleport Pottery   SER 1479b

Type:	Clay preparation plant
Maker & Date:	Wm Boulton, Burslem, 1888-90 to 1930
Photo Taken:	1975
Cylinder/dimensions:	
Hp:	*Rpm:* *Psi:*
Service:	China clay preparation

The main drive, from the engine (SER 1479a) was by spur gears and an underground shaft at the left, and then bevel wheels and upright shafts to the pulleys and overhead belts to the machines. The large pulley on the vertical shaft in the centre was for a blunger – a stirring mechanism which prevented the clay from settling in the underground storage tanks. Soundly planned at the start it, was simple, yet highly effective, and more efficient and cheaper by far to run than electrical driving and gear boxes.

141. Burslem, Dunn, Bennett & Co, Dalehall Pottery   SER 1412

Type:	Horizontal single cylinder non-condensing
Maker & Date	Maker unknown. c. 1880s?
Photo Taken:	1970
Cylinder/dimensions:	13in x 1ft 10in – Slide valve
Hp: 40	*Rpm:* 85 *Psi: 100*
Service:	Works driven by 11in belt off 6ft 0in flywheel

This was purchased for under £50 second-hand in 1945 and was in regular use at the works in the 1970s, providing power for part of the clay preparation plant. The exhaust steam was used in drying kilns at 10psi, a large amount of steam also being used directly from the boilers. It drove two clay mixing blungers, filter presses and two hydraulic press pumps. A riding cut-off valve was fitted on the back of the main slide valve, under the control of a shaft governor which was highly effective. The engine was maintained in good condition and it was intended to retain it in service as it was very economical. Latterly, with increasing demand, the pug or extruding presses, which shaped the prepared clay ready for the throwing, were converted to electric motor drive.

142. Burslem, Dunn, Bennett & Co, Dalehall Pottery   SER 1412a

Type:	Press and filter pumps
Maker & Date:	No data
Photo Taken:	1970
Service:	Clay preparation

The clay was received directly from the pits and thoroughly mixed to a watery fluid, screened to extract any stones, and then delivered to the storage tanks below the floor. It is transferred as needed to the blungers which are chambers with agitators which keep it at an even consistency. The final stages of manufacture are transfer from the blungers to the filters, firstly by the pumps seen at the right through pressing sheets, and finally in the high pressure filters where the rest of the moisture is pressed out. The clay is delivered to the pug presses where, under heavy pressure, it was formed into shapes suitable for the final shaping into pottery. It is really the traditional system with mechanical aids, producing very high-grade products. Finely ground calcined flint and other ingredients are added in the storage tanks and blungers.

143. Burslem, Norton Colliery   SER 351

Type:	Cornish beam	
Maker & Date:	Sandys, Vivian, Hayle, 1859	
Photo Taken:	1949	
Cylinder/dimensions:	64in x 9ft 0in – Cornish valves	
Hp: ?	*Spm:* 8-12	*Psi:* 45
Service:	Mine water pump. 98 gallons per stroke	
	220 yards lift by two 18in ram pumps	

Norton was a busy pit turning out 11,000 tons of coal per week in the early 1950s, from seams 440 yds. deep. This was called the *Dinah Pumping Engine*, the name and data as above being painted on the timber lagging of the cylinder. It had long been a standby to the electric pumps which latterly pumped from the full depth. The colliery was largely unaltered until the later 1950s when major re-arrangements were projected. The winders were Worsley Mesnes, similar to Holditch;possibly the pit was owned by the same concern?

144. Darlaston, Canal Pumping Station, Herbert's Park   SER 491

Type:	Woolf compound Cornish underbeam	
Maker & Date:	Hathorn, Davey & Co, Leeds, No 6135, c. 1906?	
Photo Taken:	1952	
Cylinder/dimensions:	25in x 6ft 0in and 45in x 8ft 0in – Drop valves	
Hp:	*Rpm:*	*Psi:*
Service:	Returned water to top lock pound	

This was little used when seen and no details could be secured, being unattended, but it was in use as required, raising water for the canal. It was the pure Davey Cornish cycle engine, with steel plate under beam, and possibly with plunger pumps, but the depth and sizes were unobtainable. The mahogany timber lagging upon the hot surfaces was very complete, scarcely any metal being exposed. The high pressure cylinder can be seen to the right of the tall low pressure one.

145. Darlaston, Canal Pumping Station, Herbert's Park   SER 491a

Type:	Engine House
Maker & Date:	
Photo Taken:	1952
Cylinder/dimensions:	
Hp:	*Rpm:* *Psi:*
Service:	

This was a typical Staffordshire brick structure, plain but substantial. The engine was driven from the upper platform on the level of the doorway seen at the top and the house was over 30ft high, 24ft wide, and 20ft long. The pumps were probably underneath the engine but this could not be checked. The exhaust pipe and the condenser air pump can be seen at the left of the engine house. The boiler can be seen near the base of the chimney, which was about 70ft high. All was probably dismantled in the 1950s.

146. Draycott in the Moors, Staffordshire Potteries Water Board, Cresswell Pumping Station   SER 1467

Type:	2 Inverted vertical triple expansion engines
Maker & Date:	Hathorn, Davey & Co., Leeds, No. 7801, 1932
Photo Taken:	1974
Cylinder/dimensions:	17in, 29in & 44in x 3ft – Corliss valves
Hp: About 150 each	*Rpm:* 18 *Psi:* 160
Service:	County supply

These were the maker's latest type, with reheaters between the cylinders and drop valves off Craig valve gear for superheated steam. Lift 96ft from well, and forcing to 220ft. to the reservoir by 3 – 14in plunger pumps. The well sets were Ashley concertina type, driven by a 3-throw crankshaft over the wells. They were due to stop working in 1975. The flywheels were 14ft. in diameter.

147. Eccleshall, Staffordshire Potteries Water Board, Millmeece Pumping Station   SER 1466[1]

Type:	2 horizontal tandem Corliss valve pumping engines
Maker & Date:	One – Ashton, Frost & Co., Blackburn, 1914
	Other – Hathorn, Davey, 1926
Photo Taken:	1974
Cylinder/dimensions:	1914 = 26in & 49in x 5ft
	1926 = 27in & 52in x 5ft
Hp: About 180 each	*Rpm:* 16 *Psi:* 160
Service:	County water supply

The Ashton, Frost engine seen in the print developed a crack in the frame, and had the well pumps removed in 1938, and a motor-driven well pump installed – the Hathorn, Davey remained unaltered. The Hathorn, Davey was in regular use in 1975 and remained so until 1977. They are tandem compound rotative sets, together pumping $3\frac{1}{2}$ million gallons per day from 120ft. down, to a surface force lift of 400ft. The surface force lift pumps were directly behind the rear, LP cylinders, with the well pumps outside, twin bucket pumps – Two per engine off L beams. The Davey was the regular-duty engine, noiseless in working except for the Corliss trip gear. The Ashton, Frost well pumps had 75 hp motors. Two Lancashire boilers by Danks of 1914 and one Galloway of 1926 supplied superheated steam. The engines and pumps were over 110ft. long.

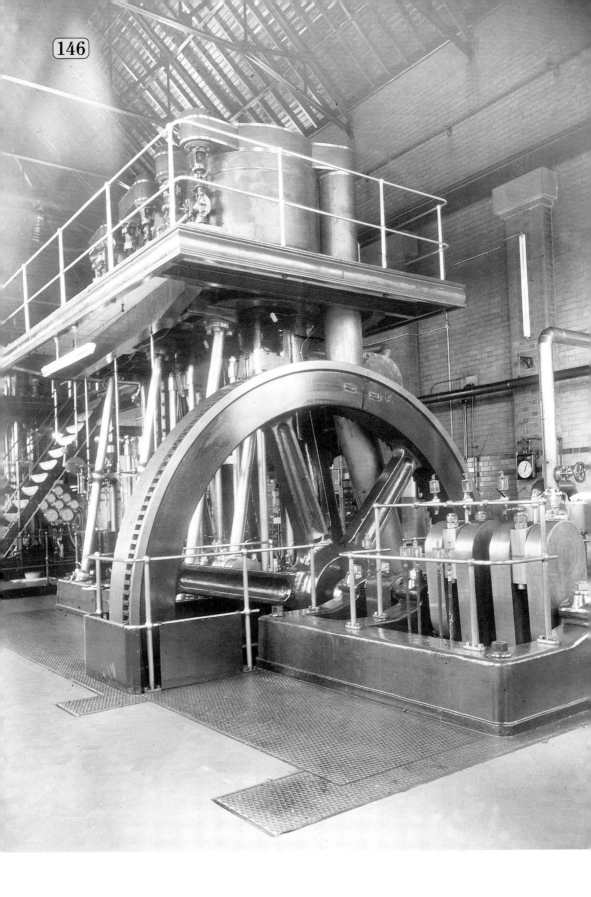

148. Eccleshall, Staffordshire Potteries Water Board, Millmeece Pumping Station   SER 1466[2]

Only photograph available (No data)

149. Fenton, Anchor Mills   SER 347

Type:	Single cylinder beam
Maker & Date:	W & J Galloway, 1851
Photo Taken:	1949
Cylinder/dimensions:	40^1/$_2$in x 6ft 0in – Slide valves
	Beam 18ft 0in centres. Flywheel 25ft 0in diameter
Hp: 200	*Rpm:* 25 *Psi:* 50
Service:	Pan mills. Flint grinding

This was built for 127 hp, being rebuilt by Galloways in 1881, with a new cylinder, and for higher pressure (original 20 psi) to give 200 hp. It drove everything: pans, pumps and roll crushers, there being 10 large flint grinding pans, as well as 28 small ones for colour grinding. An unusual feature was that it ran the opposite way to usual, i.e. the connecting rod came downwards on the cylinder side, driving through the usual ratchet and pawls, so that the drive could not be reversed, even if the engine was. Despite the heavy load, it gave little trouble.

150. Fenton, Mellor's Mills   SER 475

Type:	Single McNaughted beam
Maker & Date:	Unknown, c. 1860
Photo Taken:	1952
Cylinder/dimensions:	30in x 3ft 0in – Semi rotary valve
	36in x 6ft 0in – Slide valves
Hp: 100?	*Rpm:* 18 *Psi:* 80
Service:	Potter's flint grinding

There were probably only two McNaught compounded potter's mill beam engines, and this was converted by D. Adamson in 1896. There was usually at least one major rebuild of potter's mill beam engines during their long life, usually to increase the power. In most cases this meant a new cylinder for higher pressure, but here the original cylinder was retained, and the extra power gained by the added high pressure cylinder. Most of the simple engines still used steam at about 30-40 psi all their lives, and the economy here must have been worth while, particularly since a drop cut-off valve was fitted before the high pressure cylinder. The gear drives were complex, more pans having been added. These were driven by a shaft coupled by two gearwheels in the open air at the end of the mill building.

151. Hanley, Messrs Edwards, Flint Millers, Bucknall   SER 431

Type:	Single condensing beam
Maker & Date:	Unknown
Photo Taken:	1952
Cylinder/dimensions:	32in x 6ft 0in – Drop valves
Hp: abt 30	*Rpm*: 20 *Psi*: 5
Service:	Grinding mill drive

This ran as a low pressure unit using the exhaust steam from the Robey drop valve engine that drove the other grinding plant, which used steam at 80psi, and was probably put in c. 1900. There was also a waterwheel driving a single pan. In all there were 11 pans, 4 driven by the beam, and 6 by the Robey engine, and 1 off the waterwheel, which was 18ft 0in diameter undershot. The works closed in the early 1960s. The print shows the crankshaft and one of the several bevel drives. The whole engine could not be photographed.

152. Hanley, Jesse Shirley & Son   SER 430a

Type:	Single condensing beam
Maker & Date:	Sherratt & Co, Salford?, c. 1840s?
Photo Taken:	1951
Cylinder/dimensions:	30in x 5ft 0in – Slide valve
Hp: 85	*Rpm* 22: *Psi: 30*
Service:	Grinding mill drive.

Called *Princess*, this was said to have been secondhand when installed about 1850. It was later rebuilt by Kirks of Etruria, possibly about 1890, and had a new beam, made by Dean and Lowe of Stoke-on-Trent, fitted in 1917 when the crankpin broke, but it was not altered in other respects. Having almost certainly come from a Manchester cotton mill, it gives a good picture of what the early engine rooms looked like. The flywheel was 20ft in diameter, and there were separate valves for the top and the bottom of the cylinder. The bell seen at the top was to give the engine man advice upon handling the engine when the various mills were disconnected once the grind was completed and the mill was emptied and refilled.

153. Hanley, Jesse Shirley & Son   SER 430b

Type:	Millshaft drives
Maker & Date:	
Photo Taken:	1951
Cylinder/dimensions:	
Hp:	*Rpm*: *Psi*:
Service:	Grinding mill gearing. 10 pans

The beam engine drove the two shafts by a pinion 6ft 6in diameter to two gearwheels of l0ft 0in diameter on the shafts. There were 5 grinding pans per shaft on the floor above driven by bevel gears 3ft 6in diameter, to make 17 rpm, with alternate wheels opposed to each other to balance the thrust. All of the teeth were of cast iron, but very quiet. There were also drives for a small colour grinder, and the hoist. The whole was certainly running in 1971, and was the last working traditional pan milling layout in the trade, but due for replacement.

154. Himley, Himley Brickworks   SER 23

Type:	2 single cylinder non-condensing beam
Maker & Date:	Uncertain
Photo Taken:	1935
Cylinder/dimensions:	No. 1 = 20in x 6ft 0in – Slide valve
	No. 2 = 19¼in x 5ft 0in – Slide valve
Hp: 100each	*Rpm: 25* *Psi: 80*
Service:	Drove brick-making and clay preparation plant

These ran 120 hours per week up to 1948, using the exhaust to dry the green bricks. No. 2 engine drove 4 pairs of tempering or crushing rolls through a train of 8 spur gear wheels; as well as a tempering machine. Each of the 8 gear wheels in the drive was fitted with friction clutch. The two engines were generally similar in design, and it was odd that in later years when other preparation plant was installed the engines were kept running without load, to pass the steam to the dryers. The whole steam system was probably scrapped later when hot air dryers were fitted.

155. Hopwas, Tamworth Waterworks, Hopwas Pumping Station
SER 121

Type:	2 simple rotative beam
Maker & Date:	Gimson & Co., Leicester, 1880
Photo Taken:	1936
Cylinder/dimensions:	24in x 5ft 0in – Slide valve
Hp: 75?	*Rpm*: 20 *Psi: 35*
Service:	Town supply from wells to reservoir
	Single bucket and plunger pump per engine

Two plain engines with Meyer cut-off valves, with the pumps arranged at the end of the beam in line with the connecting-rod gudgeon pins. This meant that the inner pump rod was in line with the crankshaft, so a cast-iron bridle was fitted in the pump rod which passed around the crankshaft, to the pump rod to the well, the outer rod passing straight down into the well, to couple to the cross head and the other pump rod near the pump. It was a very unusual layout.

156. Lichfield, South Staffs Waterworks, Sandfields Pumping Station
SER 253

Type:	Cornish beam
Maker & Date:	J Davies, Tipton, Staffs
Photo Taken:	1938
Cylinder/dimensions:	65in x 9ft 0in
Hp:	*Rpm:* *Psi:*
Service:	Town supply from wells. 2 million gallons per day. 300ft head

This plant at one time contained three rotative beam engines that had served the atmospheric railway, and which were in service until superseded by the Sulzer uniflow engines in 1922. The Cornish engine was little used after that. It was a typical engine of the later period, plain but well finished, again with C collar crosshead fixing. It is an interesting commentary on boiler practice, that when the original 9 Cornish boilers for the whole plant were condemned in 1907, they were replaced by 3 Lancashire ones for 100psi. All of the boilers were removed when the motor pumps were installed.

157. Newcastle-under-Lyme, Parkhouse Colliery   SER 1354

Type:	Double cylinder horizontal
Maker & Date:	Worsley Mesnes Co., Wigan, 1919
Photo Taken:	1968
Cylinder/dimensions:	30in x 5ft? – Drop and Corliss valves
Hp: ?	*Rpm*: 35 *Psi*: 140
Service:	Coal winding. Shaft 500 yards deep
	Rope drum 10ft 6in diameter. 3 tons 10 cwt coal per wind in 4 tubs

The colliery was closed in 1968, and the site cleared, but there was only a single downcast shaft here, with a disused capstan-wound second shaft, and there must have been a drift to another colliery. This had wound up to 1,250 tubs per shift, a heavy duty since the cages were two decked, requiring two stops per wind. Some re-equipment had occurred in 1919, when Babcock water-tube boilers were installed, and possibly the mixed pressure turbine was installed then, but little record remained as the turbines were removed in 1946, as soon as nationalised. The colliery was certainly actively working coal until the early 1960s. It is probable that the coal reserves were to be worked out by the nearby Holditch Colliery. The engine was typical of the later designs suitable for the use of high steam pressures.

158. Newcastle-under-Lyme, Holditch Colliery, No1 Shaft   SER 1355a

Type:	Horizontal double cylinder
Maker & Date:	Worsley Mesnes Co., Wigan, 1918
Photo Taken:	1968
Cylinder/dimensions:	30in x 5ft 0in – Drop and Corliss valves
Hp: ?	*Rpm*: 30 *Psi*: 150
Service:	Coal winding. Shafts 660 yards deep.
	Rope drum 16ft diameter. 3 deck cages. 4ton 10cwt coal per wind

Holditch was a very efficient pit, although there was no usage of the exhaust steam and despite the three deck cages, with banking taking some 50 seconds even with pneumatic tub removal. There were 39 revolutions per wind, with a total cycle from away on one wind to away on the next of under two minutes. Tail ropes were later used, and when the engines were tried without them, following an accident elsewhere, the engines were difficult to start. No tail ropes were used for years, and without them the engines needed 120 psi to start away, so tail ropes were fitted in 1963. The result was a great help to the colliery as two boilers were shut down and the engines would run easily on 90 psi. It was reckoned that the cost of fitting the ropes was paid for in three months with a continuous saving there after. Certainly the engines work easily with them, despite the 4 tons 10 cwt payload of coal on the small engines. There were 10 Danks dish-ended boilers at the pit, 9 usually in use with poor coal. No. 2 engine was the same make, but smaller, with piston valves.

159. Norbury, Canal Repair Shops   SER 492

Type:	Table engine
Maker & Date:	Unknown
Photo Taken:	1952
Cylinder/dimensions:	12in x 1ft 6in – Slide valve
Hp: abt 12	*Rpm*: 50 *Psi*: 50
Service:	Sawmill machinery drives

Plain and simple, this had very little attention. The crankshaft was a very fine forging bent from a single bar with several collars for the connecting rod ends solid with it. It was about 8ft 3in high, the table 3ft 9in by 3ft 1in and the fly-wheel 6ft 3in diameter. The moulding on

the cast framing and top guides was attractive and the fluting upon the valve chest cover was particularly so. It was completely self contained except for the outer bearing for the crank-shaft, and probably scrapped in the 1960s.

160. Rugeley, South Staffordshire Waterworks, Brindley Bank Pumping Station   SER 1488

Type:	Horizontal rotative tandem compound
Maker & Date:	Hathorn, Davey & Co., Leeds, 1903
Photo Taken:	1975
Cylinder/dimensions:	abt 30in and 54in x 5ft – Slide valves
Hp: abt 250	*Rpm*: 10-12 *Psi*: 120
Service:	District water supply. $1\frac{1}{2}$ million gallons per day. 750ft

A massive engine 90ft long over the pumps, and with a 24ft flywheel, this ran for 66 years pumping nearly 300 million gallons per year on 2 shifts. A four-piece bed ran the whole length of the engine, with the surface force pump driven from the piston tail rod and the well-pump driven by rods from the crank pin. A Meyer riding cut-off valve was fitted to the HP cylinder and a plain slide valve on the LP, with metallic packing on the piston and soft packing on valve door spindles. The condenser air pump was driven from the disc crank on the end of the crank shaft.
It is now extremely well kept as a waterworks museum.

161. Rugeley, South Staffordshire Waterworks, Brindley Bank Pumping Station   SER 1488b

Type:	Deep well pumps
Maker & Date:	Hathorn, Davey & Co., Leeds
Photo Taken:	1975
Service:	Raising water to the surface

There were two bucket pumps down the well driven by sweep rods from the crank coupled L beams as seen either side of the capstan which was used to lift the pump rods during overhauls. The two L beams were coupled by rods which passed underneath the capstan. The flywheel had 10 arms and was made in 10 sections.

162. Smethwick, Best & Lloyd, Brassfounders   SER 849a

Type:	Four column single beam
	Peel, Williams & Peel, Manchester, c. 1840s
Photo Taken:	1957
Cylinder/dimensions:	24in x 3ft 0in – Piston valve
Hp: abt 80	*Rpm*: 40 *Psi*: 50
Service:	Works drive. Bevel wheels

This was a typical heavy industrial engine, a type which rarely failed, and was probably made for a cotton mill. It was removed when the load increased. It was said to have been installed second-hand at Bests late in the 19th century, and latterly was due to be preserved. The engine was unaltered, and probably had little repair in over a century at work, but the drive, probably by spur wheels, was altered at Bests as their works shaft was overhead and at right angles. An unusual feature was that the radius rods of the parallel motion were very short and attached to the entablature, which avoided the need for a frame around the cylinder end for the radius rods. It ceased working in the early 1960s. It remained in the works for some years after ceasing work. The maker's neat ornamental cast iron name plate was mounted above the entablature.

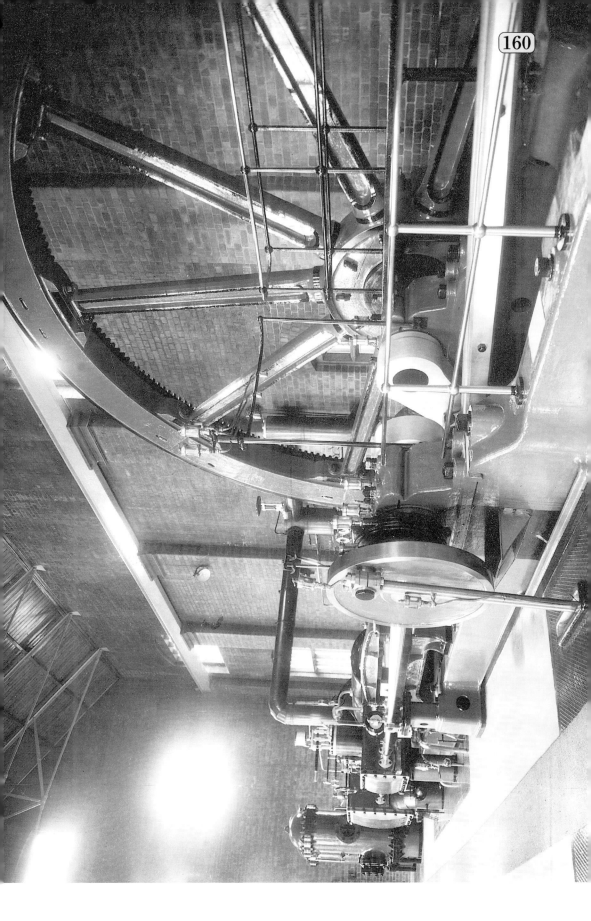

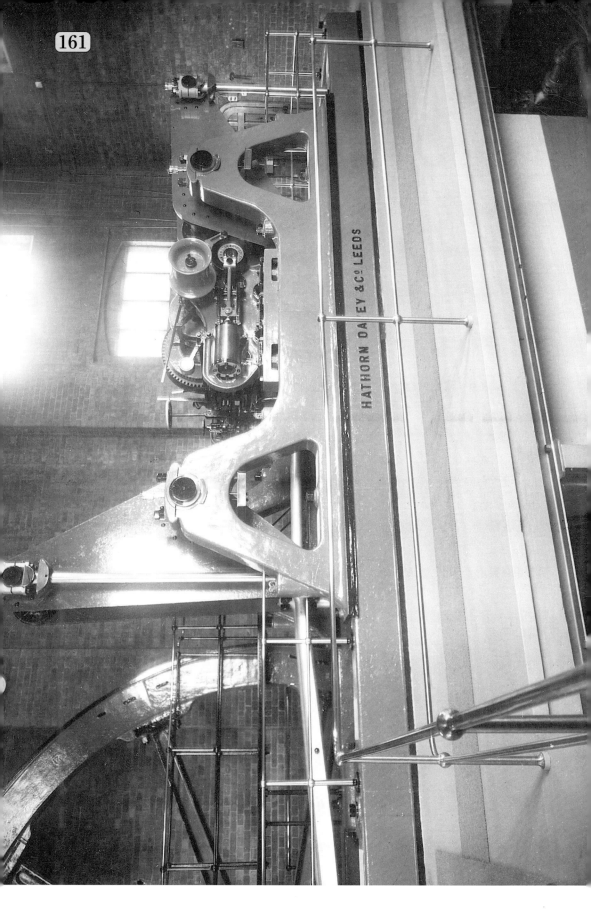

163. Smethwick, J Parkes, Albion Forge   SER 657

Type:	Cross compound horizontal condensing
Maker & Date:	Daniel Adamson & Co., 1898
Photo Taken:	1954
Cylinder/dimensions:	18in and 32in x 4ft 0in – Wheelock valves, type B
Hp: 200	*Rpm:* 90 *Psi:* 100
Service:	Ferrous rolling mills

This was said to have come from a Lancashire cotton mill, and was often heavily overloaded. Like SER 656 [See Vol. 4] this remained unaltered, needing little attention except for the valves. The forge was closed in the mid-1950s and all was scrapped. English Wheelock engines frequently had semi-rotary Corliss type valves on the low pressure cylinder as did SER 656 and 657.

164. Smethwick, Lones, Vernon & Co   SER 345

Type:	Single condensing beam
Maker & Date:	Unknown
Photo Taken:	1949
Cylinder/dimensions:	32in x 5ft 0in – Drop valves. Beam 17ft 6in centres
Hp: abt 400	*Rpm:* 20 *Psi:* 40
Service:	Rolling mill for wrought iron use

This was a typical Black Country engine, with a timber, iron strapped connecting rod, but the valve gearing differed in that the steam and exhaust valves were on the same centre line, i.e. the spindle of the upper one was tubular, with that for the lower one passing through. There was no steam cut-off, since the upper steam and the lower exhaust valve spindles were off the same vertical rod. The works made a variety of shafts and buffers for railways, using half-rolls to forge down the shanks from the solid bar. This was latterly done by a separate set of half rolls driven by a vertical engine. The entire works was scrapped later.

165. Stoke-on-Trent, Foley Mills   SER 349a

Type:	No 1 engine.
Maker & Date:	
Photo Taken:	1949
Cylinder/dimensions:	
Hp:	*Rpm:* *Psi:*
Service:	Grinding pan drives

This was unusual in that the pan drive was directly from the crankshaft, whereas there was usually a reduction gear between them. The drive off to the left by bevel wheels to another set was also uncommon.

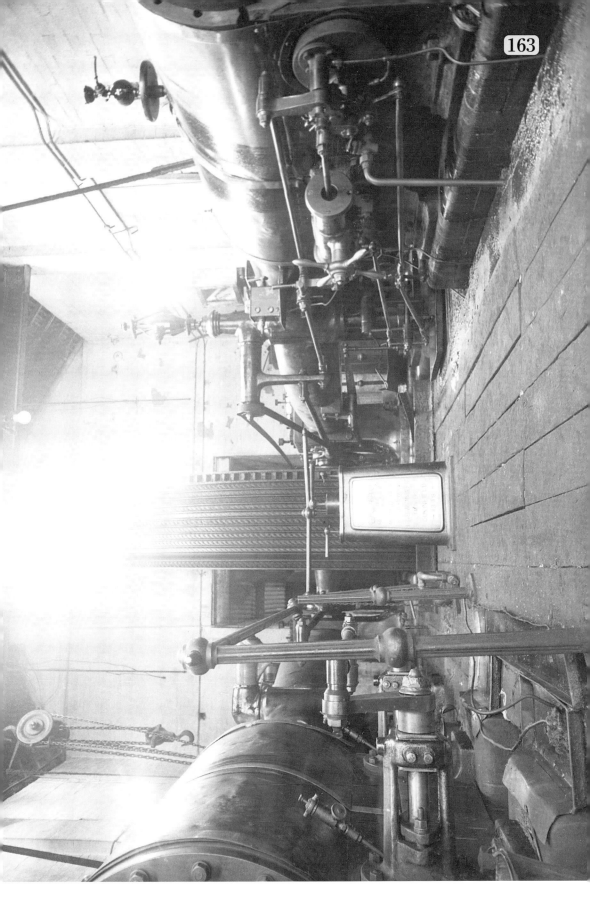

166. Stoke-on-Trent, Foley Mills

SER 349a

Type:	Two single cylinder condensing beam
Maker & Date:	John Shenton & Son, Engineers, Fenton, date ?
Photo Taken:	1949
Cylinder/dimensions:	1 = 27in x 4ft 0in – Slide valves
	2 = 30in x 5ft 0in – Slide valves
	Beam 16ft 6in centres. Flywheels 17ft 6in & 20ft diameter
Hp: 1-46, 2-67	*Rpm*: 1-33, 2-24 *Psi: 60*
Service:	Flint grinding for pottery trade

These were generally similar, but the larger had fluted columns. Typical potter's engines, each had top & bottom slide valves, with the reversed or stoup gland for the valve rod, below the valve chest. The drives were different from the usual type (see 349a & b).

167. Stoke-on-Trent, Foley Mills

SER 349b

Type:	
Maker & Date:	
Photo Taken:	1949
Cylinder/dimensions:	
Hp:	*Rpm:* *Psi:*
Service:	Grinding pan drives

One series of five grinding pans was driven by a series of large spur wheels. This required great accuracy in the setting, as the pan placement had to be that of the mesh of the gear wheels. It did work very well, but it was most unusual.

168. Stoke-on-Trent, Salisbury Colliery

SER 350

Type:	Bull type shaft pump
Maker & Date:	Possibly colliery owners?, 1895
Photo Taken:	1949
Cylinder/dimensions:	80in x 9ft 0in – Drop valves
Hp: ?	*Rpm*: 5 *Psi: 60*
Service:	Mine pump. 500 gallons per stroke lifting 600ft

This was probably made by the owners of the colliery in the workshops, as it had "*Salisbury pit 1896*" cast on an arbor bracket. It was very plain, and was technically interesting in that there was no air pump, the working vacuum being secured, as in the Newcomen engine, by a long condenser discharge pipe downhill to a low level. The vacuum varied from 15 to 22ins. The pit was closed during the reorganisations of the 1950s, and all scrapped.

169. Stoke-on-Trent, Stafford Colliery (nr Fenton)   SER 1357

Type:	Two vertical double cylinder
Maker & Date:	Makers unknown, 1880s
Photo Taken:	1968
Cylinder/dimensions:	36in x 6ft 0in – Piston valves
Hp: ?	*Rpm:* 46 *Psi:* 60
Service:	Coal winding. Shaft 904 yards deep. Rope drum 18ft diameter

This was a part of the Stafford Coal and Iron Co., started in the 1880s, which contained blast furnaces, brickworks, coke ovens and chemical manufacturing plant until 1920. It was in fact a complete highly evolved unit of good economy, but was reduced to coal drawing by 1945. The engines were very massive with the rope drums overhead, and always had piston valves. These were altered to the Worsley Mesnes automatic cut-off type when the shafts were both sunk to the full depth, as the original coal at 600 yards was worked out. With the new valves (internal piston cut-offs), steam was cutting-off at 10 of the 47 revolutions that the wind required. The average wind took 75 seconds. The continuance of the pit seemed assured in 1968 and no changes were then planned. The print shows the driver's position, between the two cylinders and facing the shaft.

170. Stretton, Burton-on -Trent Sewage Works, Clay Mills Pumping Station   SER 68

Type:	4 Woolf compound beams
Maker & Date:	Gimson & Co, Leicester, 1885
Photo Taken:	1936
Cylinder/dimensions:	24in x 6ft 0in – Drop valves
	Beams 24ft 0in long. Flywheel 24ft diameter
Hp: 150 each	*Rpm:* $10^1/_2$ *Psi:* 80
Service:	Sewage lift. 2 ram pumps per engine, 21in x 6ft 0in, one
	driven off beam. 125,000 gallons per hour each, to 110ft head

There were two engine houses, each with two engines, one engine usually at work, with the others readily available, since flooding was rapid in wet weather. One ram pump was driven from the high pressure piston tail rod, with the other driven from the beam at a similar point the other side of the beam centre. All of the auxiliary drives were by steam engines, there being at least 12 of these. The new plant completely superseded this and the Lancashire boilers, but the old plant may remain for some years.

171. Stretton, Burton-on-Trent Sewage Works, Clay Mills Pumping Station   SER 1358

Type:	Horizontal single cylinder
Maker & Date:	Buxton and Thornley, Burton-on-Trent, 1890s
Photo Taken:	1968
Cylinder/dimensions:	10in x 1ft 6in – Slide valves
Hp: About 15	*Rpm:* 100 *Psi:* 80
Service:	Station lighting plant

The station was self-supplied with over a dozen auxiliary steam engines, all horizontal or vertical slide valve types. These ran the workshop, the lime treatment, and storm water pumping units, among other duties. There were two engines in the electric light station, and the horizontal drove an early undertype dynamo by belt, as did the other vertical engine of unknown make. The horizontal was the regular duty engine, and ran for most of the time for over seventy years, as long as steam was the main power. Engine and dynamo had thus had very great use, and with care were in very good condition when the new electrical pumps and

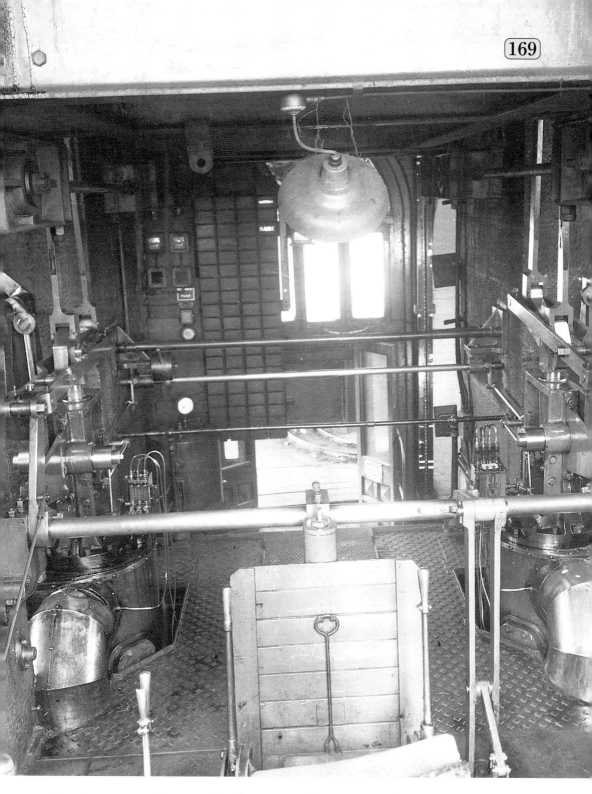

disposal system came into operation about 1968. There were several of Buxton and Thornley's small rotative pumps on general service. It was intended to preserve one of the large beam engines, and possibly it would be used for low sludging work, and the auxiliaries although disused may possibly remain. The electric light plant certainly justified saving.

172. Swynnerton, Staffordshire Potteries Water Board, Hatton Pumping Station   SER 474

Type:	Two Woolf compound condensing beam
Maker & Date:	Kirk & Co, Etruria, Stoke-on-Trent, 1892
Photo Taken:	1952
Cylinder/dimensions:	32$^1/_2$in x 4ft 4in and 48in x 7ft 0in – Slide valves
Hp: ?	*Rpm:* 16 *Psi:* 75
Service:	District supply from wells to reservoir. Pumps 18$^1/_2$in x 7ft 0in

The pumps were 30ft. down the well, and the surface head not known, but the engines pumped up to 2,000,000 gallons per day each possibly up to 400ft. head. The crankshafts caused trouble as the bearings were very wide apart and new shafts with a steady bearing were installed in 1921. After this they gave little trouble until they were superseded by electrically driven sets in the late 1940s, due to load growth. The steam plant was all scrapped in 1951-2.

173. Tunstall, W H Grindley & Co., Flint Millers   SER 493

Type:	Non-condensing Mc Naughted beam
Maker & Date:	Kidsgrove Foundry?, 1860s?
Photo Taken:	1952
Cylinder/dimensions:	25in x 2ft 06in and 30in x 4ft 6in – Semi-rotary slide valves
Hp: About 100	*Rpm:* 20 *Psi:* 100?
Service	Flint grinding. Exhaust steam to feed water heater

Known as The Legal Grinding Mill, this was unusual for the non condensing-beam engine, possibly due to water shortage at the site. It was also one of the latest McNaught compounding installations, said to have been done by the Manor Engineering Works in 1920-21. Supporting the high pressure cylinder between two columns which were attached to the upper floor was unusual, but the original engine was largely intact, except for a new crankshaft and flywheel supplied when McNaughted. The grinding pans were unusual as they were arranged upon two floors, there being a shaft up through the lower pan to drive the mill upon the upper floor, i.e. there were two mainshafts, each with two bevel wheels upon it, each driving two mills in tandem. It was probably the only layout like it, possibly so arranged when the engine was compounded? One upright shaft also drove two more pans by cotton ropes.

174. Tunstall, Chatterley-Whitfield Colliery, Hesketh Shaft   SER 1356

Type:	Double cylinder horizontal
Maker & Date:	Worsley Mesnes Co., Wigan, 1914
Photo Taken:	1968
Cylinder/dimensions:	36in x 6ft 0in - Drop and Corliss valves
Hp: ?	*Rpm:* 40 *Psi: 150*
Service:	659 yds deep. Drum 14 to 20ft diameter

Similar to, but larger than Holditch No. 1, this averaged 32 revolutions per wind, but was not coal turning (winding) so its performance was unknown. It was the last unit of a large steam system, after the two steam Walker's compressors were replaced by electrically driven turbine compressors in 1968. Seven Lancashire boilers with chain grate stokers were in use for the compressors and the one winder, but only the pit-head baths steam supply would be needed after 1970 when the last engines were scrapped. It was intended to continue coal winning at the site, once one of the largest in the district, making also bricks and coke. The air compressors were as large as any in the collieries anywhere.

175. Tunstall, Goldendale Ironworks   SER 473

Type:	Two beam blowing engines
Maker & Date:	Unknown, one c. 1833
Photo Taken:	1952
Cylinder/dimensions:	Abt 45in and 48in x 7ft 6in - Drop valves
Hp: ?	*Rpm:* 20 *Psi:* 30
Service:	Blast furnace blowing

The two engines were different, one said to have been bought when the works started in the 1840s, from an ironworks which had started in 1833, whilst the other was said to have been made on the site. Both were originally direct acting, i.e. having no crank, flywheel, or crankshaft. The crankshaft and large flywheel were added, the two engines then running together, but at a later date this was again modified by cutting the crankshaft and adding another flywheel so that either side could be run independently. Thus even by Goldendale's odd standards they were unusual, starting as one direct acting engine, then adding another, then making them rotative with the flywheels and acting together, and then splitting them to run independently. The final stage of installing a steam turbine blower was usual, and it is possible that the engines were made separate then.

176. Walsall, G. & R. Thomas Ltd, Hatherton Ironworks   SER 439a

Type:	Single cylinder rotative condensing beam
Maker & Date:	Unknown
Photo Taken:	1952
Cylinder/dimensions:	48in (steam) and 104in (air) x 9ft 6in - Drop valves
Hp:	*Rpm:*16-18 *Psi:*
Service:	Blast furnace blowing

This was the usual beam blower with equal stroke for the steam and the air cylinders, and with the crank driven off the overhung beam end, giving 10ft 9in crank stroke. Metal plates had been added to give more flywheel weight, but otherwise there had been little alteration. The timber connecting rod was 19in x 10in cross section, with iron strapping.

177. Walsall, G. & R. Thomas Ltd, Hatherton Ironworks   SER 439b

Type:	Horn beam of SER 439
Maker & Date:	
Photo Taken:	1952
Cylinder/dimensions:	36ft 0in long overall
Hp:	*Rpm:* *Psi:*
Service:	Blast furnace blowing

This was the customary horn beam of the blowing engines which was upswept to give a longer connecting rod. The twin sides or flitches were open sand castings of attractive design, and the neat circular pattern of the handrail supports added effect to what was often very plain. The engine was broken up in the early 1950s, having been idle for some time in 1948.

178. Walsall, Sevens Colliery

SER 762

Type:	Single cylinder beam condensing
Maker & Date:	Unknown
Photo Taken:	1955
Cylinder/dimensions:	24in x 5ft 0in – Drop valves
Hp: ?	*Rpm*: 20 *Psi*: 10-15
Service:	Coal winding. Shaft depth unknown

This was disused and little was known about it in the 1950s, but it was interesting for the operation of the valves from a plug rod from the parallel motion: a very early type. It possibly had the rope drum on the engine crankshaft at one time, possibly using flat ropes on reels, but latterly round ropes were used on a drum driven from the engine by spur gearwheels with equal numbers of teeth. It was unaltered, retaining the slight cast iron connecting rod, square cast iron crankshaft and timber cross beam on the top of the two columns beneath the beam centre. There were stiffening castings on the top of the columns and the timber beam had steel girder supports. The whole colliery was scrapped in the 1950s, together with this engine which was a very neat example of later 19th century Staffordshire engineering.

179. Walsall, Walker & Co., Steel Rolling Mills

SER 435

Type:	Horizontal single cylinder condensing
Maker & Date:	Maker and date unknown, c. 1880?
Photo Taken:	1952
Cylinder/dimensions:	42in x 5ft 0in – Slide valve
Hp: 400?	*Rpm*: 50-60 *Psi: 100*
Service:	Hot rolling mill drive

This was probably secondhand to the site, and the condenser almost certainly an addition as many later horizontal engines in the area were non-condensing. The use of the driving pinion on one side as a crank-pin boss was unusual, as was the square shafting, but there had certainly been several alterations. The flywheel was 24ft in diameter, and the outer pinion drove a two stand mill dated 1941. All of the gearing had 12in wide teeth, and the wheel was staked on with wooden wedges with steel filler wedges. It was probably broken up when rolling ceased around 1949. A separate cut-off valve had been removed and a plain slide valve fitted.

180. Wednesbury, John Bagnall & Co., Leabrook Ironworks

SER 248a

Type:	Single condensing beam
Maker & Date:	T Holcroft, Bilston, c. 1860
Photo Taken:	1938
Cylinder/dimensions:	43in x 6ft 10in - Drop valves
Hp: 500	*Rpm*: 18 *Psi*: 40-60
Service:	Rolling mill drive

Another typical Black Country engine, this had at least two accidents. One of the beam flitches failed, and was replaced by an odd one, which remained in use until the works closed, but a more serious crash was in 1938, when a crosshead failure broke the cylinder cover, and various other parts. Repairs were soon completed, including a re-bore of the air pump, and extensive re-blocking of the wood fillings in the wheel work. The drives in this were similar to SER 247.

181. Wednesbury, John Bagnall & Co., Leabrook Ironworks   SER 248b

Type:	Single cylinder non-condensing beam
Maker & Date:	James Davies, Wednesbury
Photo Taken:	1938
Cylinder/dimensions:	18in x 3ft 6in – Slide valve
Hp: 20-30	*Rpm*: 40 *Psi*: 40
Service:	Roll turning drive

This was the last surviving beam engine-driven roll turning plant of the old type, but others with other engine types did remain. The engine was the simplest possible and sturdy, and the long train of reduction gearing reduced the roll speed in the lathe to about 2 revolutions per minute. A typical small Black Country layout, it was scrapped with the rest of the plant, in the 1950s.

182. Wolverhampton, Wolverhampton Waterworks, Tettenhall Pumping Station   SER 800

Type:	Inverted vertical triple expansion
Maker & Date:	Galloways Ltd, Manchester, 1910
Photo Taken:	1956
Cylinder/dimensions:	19in, 29$\frac{1}{2}$in and 46in x 3ft 6in – Corliss valves
Hp: 250	*Rpm*: 23 *Psi*: 160
Service:	Town supply from reservoir.

This pumped 3 million gallons per day into the town reservoirs, by ram pumps below the engine. Each engine was separate, although connected to a single crankshaft as usual, but with a flywheel on either side of the central intermediate cylinder. All of the steam plant was scrapped in the general change-over in the 1950s, including the beam engines noted at the same station.

183. Wolverhampton, Wolverhampton Waterworks, Tettenhall Pumping Station   SER 39a

Type:	Cornish beam
Maker & Date:	R & W Hawthorn, 1852
Photo Taken:	1936
Cylinder/dimensions:	48in x 8ft 0in, no other data. Beam 25ft 0in long
Hp:	*Rpm*: *Psi*:
Service:	Town supply. No well. 1 plunger pump 8ft stroke

This engine was probably installed at Goldthorn Hill and removed when contamination was suspected in 1858. It was a standard waterworks engine of the period, which had been well maintained. It was probably moved by J. Watt & Co., and continued in service until the Galloways triple expansion engine (SER 39c) superseded it. There was a well at Goldthorn Hill, but the use of local well supplies was generally discontinued when the epidemics of the mid 19th century made pure water supplies a statutory requirement. This made the local stations largely re-pumping units. It is known that the stream providing the power for Town Cotton Mill at Bridgnorth was diverted to supply water to Wolverhampton, and compensation had to be given to the mill.

184. Wolverhampton, Wolverhampton Waterworks, Tettenhall Pumping Station
SER 39b

Type:	Cornish beam
Maker & Date:	Hathorn, Davey & Co, Leeds, 1885
Photo Taken:	1936
Cylinder/dimensions:	56in x 9ft 0in. Beam 25ft 0in long
Hp:	*Rpm:* *Psi:*
Service:	Town supply. 1 plunger pump 9ft 0in stroke

This was built for operation by the Davey differential gearing, without any provision for Cornish gear. The piston rods were cottered to the crossheads and the spring beams were built-up box girders. Ornament was limited to fluted equilibrium pipes, and the valve chest covers. Both of the Cornish engines were steam jacketed by having the steam entry into the jacket space itself.

185. Wolverhampton, Wolverhampton Waterworks, Tettenhall Pumping Station
SER 39c

Type:	Invertical triple expansion engine
Maker & Date:	W & J Galloway, Manchester, 1910
Photo Taken:	1936
Cylinder/dimensions:	19in, 29in and $46^{1}/_{2}$in x 3ft 6in – Corliss valves
Hp: 256	*Rpm:* 23 *Psi:* 160
Service:	3 rams pumps below. 3,000,000 gallons per day

A plain but well made engine, this ran regularly until 1950, when electric pumps were installed. The use of three separate engines each resting upon cross girders with the beds sunk below the floor made an accessible layout. The single cylinder inclined barring engine was unusual in a waterworks.

186. Wombourn, Bilston Waterworks, Bratch Pumping Station
SER 761

Type:	Two inverted vertical triple expansion
Maker & Date:	James Watt & Co. and Thornewill & Warham, 1897
Photo Taken:	1955
Cylinder/dimensions:	Sizes unknown – Corliss valves
Hp:	*Rpm:* *Psi:*
Service:	Town supply from wells

These were believed to be the last engines made by James Watt & Co. before they closed in 1896, and were thought to have been in Watt's works incomplete, and removed to Thornewills for completion. They have Thornewill & Warham's name-plate and works numbers 699 and 700 on the columns. There were cast iron columns at the front and back with the well pump drives from the inner ends of the engines to the wells, which were in an annexe in the back of the engine house, and driving by bell cranks from the horizontal rods. The Corliss valves were all at the front of the cylinders, and removal was difficult, the available space very limited. The engines were left *in situ* when electrically driven pumps were installed, working in the well in the 1950s. The buildings are very attractive.

ENGINE MAKERS INDEX

Manufacturer	SER No	Plate No
Adamson, D., & Co.	657	163
Ashton, Frost & Co.	891c	102
	890	105
	1466(1)	147
Bellis & Marcom	1418	35
	1483	129
Bever, Dorling	126	57
Blair, Campbell & McLean	1426	29
Booth & Co.	46a	114
Butterley Co.	188a	10
	22	34
	196b	84
Bradley & Craven	1502	64
Buxton & Thornley	1358	171
Clay Cross Co.	188b	11
Cockerill J.	1038	31
Daglish R., & Co.	1368b	109
	1369	113
	1372b	119
Davies, J.	253	156
	248b	181
Davy Bros	21a	89
Easton & Amos	116	92
Easton & Anderson	148a	68
	118	128
Fairbairn, Lawson, Combe, Barbour	891b	102
Fenton, Murray & Wood	196a	83
Fraser & Chalmers	1484a	44
Fullerton, Hodgart & Barclay	991a	80
Galloways Ltd	1072	32
	347	149
	800	182
	39c	185
Gimson & Co.	120	50
	1482a	51
	121	155
	68	170
Glenfield Co.	1426	29
Glenfield & Kennedy	1426	29
Graham & Co.	56	14
Grange Iron Co.	1368c	110
Gwynne & Co.	46c	116
Handyside A.,	1197a	20
Harvey, W., & Co.	436a	130

Manufacturer	SER No	Plate No
Hathorn Davey & Co.	39b	184
	891a	101
	491	144
	1467	146
	1466(1)	147
	1488	160
Hawthorn, R. & W.	25a	18
	24a	124
	1488b	161
Hick, B., & Son	42	126
Holcroft T.	248a	180
Kidsgrove Foundry	493	173
Kirk & Co.	474	172
Kitson & Co.	256	19
Lamberton & Co.	991	79
Lilleshall Co.	1171	28
Markham & Co.	1196	24
	1494b	99
	1195	100
	1367	104
	1371c	112
Marshall, Sons & Co.	1501	73
	1398	87
Musgrave J., & Sons Ltd	994a	1
	1279	15
	122	53
Naysmith, Wilson	388b	96
Neilson & Co.	119	41
Oliver & Co.	1170	16
Peel, Williams & Peel	849a	162
Petrie, J., & Co.	259a	47
	763	48
	147	71
Richardsons	992a	76
Robey & Co.	1480	17
	1399	81
	1364	107
Ryde & Co.	123	46
Sandys, Vivian	351	143
Savages	516c	59
Saxon G., Ltd	1228	5
Sheepbridge Co.	1400	4
Shenton, J., & Son	349a	165
Sherratt & Co.	430a	152
Stott, S. S, & Co.	1172	60
Tangyes Ltd	809	13
	1493	125
	1359a	138
Thornewill & Warham	1363a	8
	254	33
	1494a	98

Manufacturer	SER No	Plate No
Thornewill & Warham	1365	106
	387b	121
	1366a	122
	761	186
Tickle, J.	1173	63
Trowell	125b	38
Tuxford & Co.	195	85
Waddle Patent Fan & Engineering Co.	1197c	22
Warner & Sons	1368a	108
Willans & Robinson	734	123
Wood J., & Co.	1370	26
	1361a	42
	1371a	111
Wood & Gee	1437a	39
	1437b	40
Watt, J. & Co.	124	54
	148b	69
	148c	70
	24c	127
	252	136
	761	186
Whitham, J., & Co.	24b	97
Worsley Mesnes Co.	1363b	9
	1362	55
	1419	56
	388a	95
	1354	157
	1355a	158
	1356	174
Unknown	393	3
	1221a	6
	1221b	7
	190	27
	1436	36
	125a	37
	1361a	42
	320	43
	1362	55
	194a	74
	146	88
	117	91
	386	118
	387a	120
	436b	131
	437	132
	476	133
	438	134
	1412	141
	475	150
	431	151
	492	159

Manufacturer	SER No	Plate No
Unknown	345	164
	349a	166
	350	168
	1357	169
	473	175
	439a	176
	439b	177
	762	178
	435	179

Non Stationary Engine Makers Index

Manufacturer	SER No	Plate No
Clay preparation plant	1479b	140
	1412a	142
	491a	145
Cornish boiler	124	54
Engine houses, Soss Drainage Stn.	46d	117
Engine houses, Brindley Heath	252a	137
Flint mill	349b	167
Gas Engines	992b	77
	992c	78
Hydraulic coalwagon lifter	1175	62
Mill buildings	1194	12
Morton Colliery	1197d	23
Pug Mill	1482b	52
Shaft drive	763a	49
	430b	153
Traction Engine	453a	25
	572	67
	516b	72
	517	86
	573	93
Tractor, Steam	571	65
	571a	66
Waddle Fan	1197b	21
	1197d	23
	1484b	45
Waterwheels (incl Scoop wheels)	194b	75
	196	82
	21b	90
	46b	115
Water turbine	994b	2

SERIES EDITOR, TONY WOOLRICH

Tony was born in Bristol in 1938. He became interested in technical history in his school days.

He trained as a craftsman in the engineering industry, and from 1970 has combined his craft and historical skills in modelmaking for museums and heritage projects.

He has also published books and articles on aspects of technical history and biography. A particular interest is industrial espionage of the 18th century. Another interest is 18th century and early 19th century technical books and encyclopaedias, in particular Rees's *Cyclopædia,* (1802-1819). He has been working on a biography of the engineer John Farey, jr (1791-1851) for the past 20 years.

Since 1989 he has been heavily involved cataloguing for the National Monuments Record, Swindon, the Watkins Collection on the Stationary Steam Engine. He is also a constant consultee to the Monuments Protection Programme of English Heritage.

Since 1994 he has been acting as a contributor to the New *Dictionary of National Biography* working on biographies of engineers and industrialists. He is a contributor to the *Biographical Dictionary of Civil Engineers,* published by the Institution of Civil Engineers, 2002

He has recently completed for Wessex Water plc a study of the water supplies of Bridgwater, Wellington (Somerset) and Taunton, and was part of the team setting up the company's education centres at Ashford (near Bridgwater) and Sutton Poyntz (near Weymouth).

ACKNOWLEDGEMENTS

Thanks are due to Keith Falconer who had the foresight to acquire the collection for the RCHME, and to Helga Lane, (late of the RCHME Salisbury office) who made the original computer database of the Steam Engine Record.

Much help in the production of these volumes has been given by David Birks, National Monuments Record Archives Administration Officer; Anna Eavis, Head of Enquiry and Research Services, and the members of the public search room staff at Swindon.

Colin Bowden and Jane Woolrich did the often-difficult proof checking.

Many thanks to John Cornwell for providing the photographs of the author.

The series publishes George Watkins's texts as he wrote them and it is acknowledged that he did make mistakes. While obvious spelling and typing errors have been changed, to begin to rewrite his work in the light of present-day knowledge is an impossible task.

The Publisher and Editor welcome constructive comments from readers. Where appropriate, these will be incorporated into volume 10.